Within my memory this is clearly the first exploration of the High End Audio phenomenon of such depth and originality. Made possible, as I sincerely believe, only through Misha's knowledge, experience and enthusiasm.

— MAXIM SEMEYKIN,
Editor-In-Chief, *Audiomagazin*

In this book Misha Kucherenko has looked at our industry with a depth no one else has attempted.

— TERRY DORN,
Former President, *Audio Research Corporation*

It seems that a man exactly like Misha Kucherenko — an educated, erudite music lover, as I've known him for three and a half decades — was needed to blend together technical savvy and classical breadth, melomania and audiophilia, music and sound. Misha managed to do just that — which I deeply respect and, let's face it, even envy.

— ALEXANDER KAN,
Music critic, BBC reporter,
Author of *Kuryokhin: A Skipper On a Captain*
and *Until the Jazz Starts*

There are two main fractions in the Music Lovers' Party: melomaniacs are interested mostly in music itself, while audiophiles pay attention mostly to the sound quality. I am a hardcore melomaniac, and I'd rather listen to my favorite recordings on any lo-fi gadget than to any banal musical drivel however magnificently it is presented. My old buddy Misha Kucherenko is one of the audiophile ideologists, which see sonic ambience and the recordings' subtlest nuances as important (probably, even more important) than the melodies and the rhythms. It is a little too late to convert me to the audiophile creed, but the book can introduce the newcomers to a wonderful and intriguing new world, which the author describes with the utmost authority.

— ARTEMY TROITSKY,
Rock journalist, music critic, TV and radio host, author

There is only one person on the planet who ponders beyond the artistic expression of presenting music through electronics and into the essence of High End Audio: it is our beloved Misha Kucherenko. Misha has dedicated his life not just to the pursuit, but to the definition of the philosophy of High End Audio. Dive deep and wonder! Like Big Misha does, inspiring us all to strive towards the Greater Good.

— EVEANNA MANLEY,
President, *Manley Labs*

Working with Misha Kucherenko on our album, *Heart On Snow*, became one of the most exciting adventures of my life. His taste and expertise in selecting the repertoire, the musicians, the most fitting studios, as well as his sonic experience, allowed the album to acquire the best sound possible. During the recording process, we repeatedly returned to the topic of sound quality in our conversations, and I am infinitely grateful to Misha for significantly expanding my horizons in this area.

— MARC ALMOND,
Singer

It is always the greatest of pleasures to observe Misha Kucherenko's train of thought. His often highly unorthodox ideas always stimulate one's imagination. As does his *StereoPravda*. I would be very interested to see how my life would have changed had I read this book when I was "fourteen years old'.

— MARK LANGTHORNE,
Author of *Somebody To Love: The Life, Death and Legacy of Freddy Mercury* and *83 Minutes: The Doctor, the Damage, and the Shocking Death of Michael Jackson*

My very good friend, "Big Misha" is a perfection-appreciative audiophile and creator of leading-edge performance earphone technologies. Misha's dedication to advancing and perfecting High End Audio reproduction is to be commended. In this book, Misha shares his knowledge, experience, and passion for the pursuit of audio nirvana. As a friend for many years, we have spent countless hours exploring what it means to present music as an artistic expression and up-lifting experience. He is a truly inspiring and caring person who can teach us much.

— GARY REBER,
Editor-In-Chief & Publisher,
Widescreen Review and *Custom Home Theatre Design*

This book is about the search for the "Holy Grail of Audio': a mythological and ontological Odyssey... And as sound is, in fact, holy, finding the way to truly hearing its message is an important endeavor for every human being...

— BORIS GREBENSHIKOV,
Musician, singer, songwriter

IN ASSOCIATION WITH
GINTS GUKS OF PRO1

MISHA KUCHERENKO

StereoPravda — A Politically Incorrect View On High End Audio. — Saint Petersburg: "Time Machine Books" publishing house, 2022. — 352 p., ill.

ISBN: 978-5-6047502-2-3

The unique book you are holding in your hands is dedicated to what has been known since the 70s as the High End Audio industry (and, first and foremost, to the equipment that is at the frontline of humanity's pursuit of sonic Utopia). It describes the dramatic story of the search for High End Audio's sonic Holy Grail: the glamour and the misery, the gains and the losses, the highs and the lows. Here is a story about us, of how and why we listen, what we strive for and what we are as listening and, more importantly, *hearing* beings.

   StereoPravda brings us back to the roots. Whatever the author may be up to in this book — designing and manufacturing his own High End Audio equipment, earning his own chapter in BBC DJ John Peel's autobiography, taking ocean cruises with some of the greatest music producers of all time, or out of many other personal endevors and adventures he dwells upon in this audio saga, himself producing Marc Almond's "Russian" album — is always marked here with a vibrant immediacy, a sense of humor, as well as genuine whole-hearted love for music and truly the best possible ways to liberate it from all the hardware's constraints and to allow it to freely enrich your soul and mind.

ISBN 978-5-6047502-2-3

9 785604 750223

WWW.TIMEMACHINEBOOKS.RU
WWW.STEREOPRAVDA.COM

48 color insert pages' illustrations, the book's front inner cover and its back inner cover (from the original edition of the book, off-set printed in Russia) can be found in full original resolution and color here: **https://stereopravda.com/books/299**

MISHA KUCHERENKO

STEREO
PRAVDA

POLITICALLY
INCORRECT VIEW ON **HIGH END AUDIO**

TIME MACHINE BOOKS
Saint Petersburg
2022

TABLE OF CONTENTS

EDITOR'S WORD

High End Audio is an often misleading and too general term, it casts its shadow over the plethora of things that look closely related between themselves — but are quite dissimilar in fact: the research in human ear's sensitivity, the elation and the boosted self-appreciation that any purchase of a status symbol provides, the genuine technical masterpieces that transport you to the highest reaches of sound Utopia, the widest choice of gadgets that are no more that "polished steam engines" — and some whimsical exotics.

The book in your hands is unique, its mission is to reintroduce the very phenomenon of High End Audio in its historical and technical contexts, in its philosophy, ideology and aesthetics.

It's written by a person who is a part of the movement for 30 years already — as an enthusiast, as a local distributor of the most revered manufacturers, an ardent chronicler and even as a designer and maker of a very original audio equipment.

He is not only one of the first professionals who witnessed the emergence of High End Audio in Russia, but all these decades Misha was and still is a part of its inner workings, he rides the dynamic loop of the industry's ups and downs.

The combination of his talents and his involvement, a wealth of his experience makes one question the very possibility of another work with equal level of expertise being published here in Russia in foreseeable future.

The book goes back to the roots of High End Audio, it scrapes off the solidified layers of misconceptions and vulgarization from its very core.

You'll get a much more wholesome and valid picture than a simmering multitude of mass media publications can provide.

As a part of the recent Sound Studies discourse in the world and in Russia the book takes a stand in assessing the audio phenomena of daily life with clarity, it's an oasis of common sense.

There are things that even audio aesthetes rarely think about on their quest for the ultimate perfection. But no matter where your road takes you after reading *StereoPravda*, you won't be able to listen to the sound the way you used to, your *hearing* changes.

The book is equally practical and contemplative, it reintroduces the basic principles and forgotten axioms that even the most zealous sound conoisseurs tend to overlook despite their simplicity — or probably because of it.

This is also a very personal work. The intricate curves of the author's destiny are shaped by the global history's course, they make his view of High End Audio's past, present and — more importantly — future highly original.

Whatever Big Misha is doing — developing some hi-end hardware, taking a whole chapter of John Peel's book all to himself, cruising an ocean with Alan Parsons or producing Marc Almond's "Russian" album — it is all done with vivacity, the sense of humor and selfless devotion to the music and genuinely hi-end sound.

To be listened to in the spirit in which it was made.

— **Instructions on a vinyl record sleeve**
(England, mid-60s)

FOREWORD

In the beginning there was the Sound...

After thousands of years of music permeating all the areas of human culture the ability to separate its recorded *sound* from the sound of its live performance appeared just less than a hundred and fifty years ago.

This bifurcation, with the efforts of a handful of brave men led by Thomas Edison, split in two the components of music's direct impact on the listener, that is, it separated reactions to the technical aspects of the "transition in time" from the immediate reactions of listeners to the music itself within the aesthetic experience as a whole. Today all commercial aspects of reproducing and distributing audio information are built into this divide.

Throughout the evolution of audio equipment the process developed along several different vectors. Some were expanding the *breadth* of technology, maximizing its market penetration, while others were directed at expanding the technology's *depth* (or, rather, *height*), maximizing the quality of musical content transmitted.

It is no coincidence that the second vector of perfecting audio equipment was named *High End Audio*, as attempts to "turn back the time" cannot be successful unless every available resource is fully mobilized. Furthermore, not only do the *objective* characteristics of the equipment itself (transmission) determine the possible transmission-depth of the relayed musical content, but it is the *subjective* intention and capability of its consumers (reception) that ultimately matters most.

From its very inception until the present day High End Audio has occupied and continues to be in the intersection of *technology* and *art*. Objective technical aspects of the systems' performance and functionality can only exist in a continuum with the subjective nature of the intentions and the depths of the investigative quest on both sides of the equation: that of the manufacturer (and their various representatives) and that of the consumer.

Given all that a simple listing of significant High End Audio brands is unlikely to be familiar even to the most committed music aficionados. Opening a specialized High End Audio magazine for the first time is akin to getting your hands on a book of rare, peculiar, even *mythical* creatures which would simultaneously be a catalogue of an haute couture fashion show. This bestiary would be full of unfamiliar breeds and written in an unknown language. These astounding species could be purchased, but only at a mysterious store — and often for huge sums of money. Many of these creatures (*Apogee Acoustics*, for instance) are already either extinct or endangered — which, to be fair, only increases their value.

Mark Levinson, Audio Research, Manley, Magnepan, Krell, Legacy Audio, Martin Logan, Wilson Audio: for the uninitiated, no matter how interested they are in music, these names do not ring any bells.

Nevertheless, "we are what we listen to." Unlike a similar thesis in nutrition studies, when applied to spiritual nourishment, this truism, applicable to any "extensions of man" (as our feelings and the media that perpetuates them were termed by Marshall McLuhan) is not well regarded by the general public. All the more interesting then, how rarely we divert our attention from the music that we are listening to and are prepared to explore to the *medium* through which we do that. We rarely change the mental perspective from music to sound, and from the character of that sound to its natural or technical source, with the full range of unique opportunities that such a contemplation offers.

Although the book you are holding in your hands is undoubtedly dedicated to what has been known since the 70s' as the High End Audio industry (and, first and foremost, to the equipment that is at the frontline of humanity's pursuit of sonic Utopia), the dramatic story — of the pursuit for High-End, its glamour and its misery, the gains and the losses, the highs and the lows — described here is, in fact, a story about us. It is a story of how and why we listen, what we strive for, and what we represent as listening and, more importantly, *hearing* beings. This book is an attempt to understand what stands between us and the music we identify ourselves with as well as a blatant rehabilitation of the enduring value of what is referred to (albeit in vain) as "our soul's elation." Also it discovers and describes ways of eliminating obstacles on the way to achieving a personal resonance with it. What awaits us in this book is an examination of the borders between the coveted and the real, the palpable and the imaginary.

Throughout its history, High End Audio has remained a bone of contention, provoking rage and curses from some, wonder and awe from others. These holy audio wars destroy not only grand hopes, but sometimes also the last remnants of common sense, creating confused minds and empty hearts. Simply visit any of the numerous High End Audio Internet forums, which have blossomed all over the world to fill the void left by the waning expert audio press, to see proof of it.

The irreconcilable polarization of opinions has both a superficial and a deep-rooted explanation.

When, in the early 2000s, I was lucky enough to conduct a series of interviews with many of the industry's preeminent figures[1] for the Russian publication *Audiomagazin* the only one to turn me down was the "great and terrible" J. Gordon Holt, the founder of *Stereophile*, a magazine that played a truly pivotal role in my life. To my suggestion of talking about the current crisis of the industry he gave me a curt and unequivocal reply: "In recent years High-End has turned into a mechanism of duping simpletons of the stupider kind, and I find it disgusting to even talk about it." Such pessimism expressed by a former idealist who was a key figure at the inception of the entire phenomenon half a century ago, reveals a genuine tragedy. At the same time equally tragic is the kind of aggressive nihilism, the flip side of the coin of today's universal access to the unfiltered expression of one's own opinion on yet another specialized Internet forum where, unlike the expert communities and media sources of the past, indulging one's militant ignorance is the guiding principle.

But today's priests of the High-End Temple, bloated from conceit and a sense of self-importance, are perhaps far more toxic. The augurs of the audio industry dispense accusations of heresies of

---

[1] I even managed to get to the recluse Harry Pearson, the founder of *The Absolute Sound* magazine, buttering him up with a CD box set of the complete recordings of Lyudmila Zykina, his beloved traditional Russian folk singer.

every kind left and right in the noble tradition of holy wars — and increasingly resemble charlatans.

In 1990 I was staying with my friend Alan Robinson in San Francisco on my first visit to the US. I accidentally picked up a mostly black-and-white brochure with the weird name *Stereophile* from a pile of newspapers and magazines of every kind scattered across the coffee table. In that moment I couldn't imagine that by opening the magazine I was beginning a new chapter in my life. That event drastically changed my fate. The world of audio overwhelmed me to such an extent that traveling to my first High End Audio exhibition in Los Angeles two years later I did not hesitate over the fact that the trip cost me the equivalent of buying a studio apartment in Moscow at the time.

Stereophile magazine was unlike anything I had ever read regarding sound and audio equipment. It had a feeling, a taste of the *initiation*, a hint at the existence of a special inner circle where one would be privy not only to the skills needed to gain a nontrivial listener's experience, but to the entirely different attitude — not only towards music itself, but also the *process of perceiving it*. My passion for a pursuit of further musical proficiency was ignited at the very peak of audio's "golden age", when — which is symptomatic — unending heated debates between the editors and manufacturers in publications like this one were taken for granted. I lost myself in reading and devoured every issue "cover to cover" for years to come.

I am convinced that this turn of fate was no mere accident. The vector of my life has always been directed towards music since my student days at the Moscow Institute of Physics and Engineering (where I earned a degree in solid-state physics) when the company

I would keep consisted mostly of amateur musicians and passionate music fans. Also my English language skills — advanced for my social circle — also played their role ensuring that I wasn't cut off from the main sources of musical knowledge, the depth of which determined the extent of my subsequent engagement with the subject.

But most importantly, at the time of my initial contact with High End Audio, I found myself in a peculiar state of hard-to-define dissatisfaction. It was a vague feeling of *thirst* and *anticipation*, familiar to many music connoisseurs which in hindsight seems to me as a completely natural process: a malady of growth, a crisis of transition. Some are driven to a gloom of abundance, snobbery and disillusionment by this state. Others are inspired to embark on a search of the "authentic", dwelling among the pygmies of the rain forest or in the wards for the mentally ill, on a melting glacier or among the elephants at a Thai zoo. Some regress, insisting on listening to only vinyl records or even only to compact cassette tapes, the fad for the latter has totally out of blue arrived to the audiophiles' sandbox several years ago. In all such sad cases, whatever one is searching for, already vague, dissolves completely. It leaves a person tired, indifferent and, crucially (and it is only at first glance that this seems paradoxical) — entirely removed from music. As an old Russian saying goes: "Go there, I don't know where. Bring to me I don't know what".

But is this situation really that surprising?

When I think about that inner thirst that is at the heart of the High End Audio obsession, I am often reminded of a drawing from a respectable audio magazine from the late 90s. A futuristic audio system — grandeur and tranquility personified! — towering within an observatory dome against the blue sky as if symbolizing the pinnacle attained by humanity in its strive for perfection when, supposedly, *the sky is the limit.*

Should one descend to the ground? Or should one stay on the long and winding road towards the High Limit, enthralled by mirages, having completely lost the ability to discern between fact and fiction, between the primary and the secondary, at a risk of completely losing direction — getting hopelessly entangled in proverbial audiophile-grade cables?

In the absence of fundamental value signposts and basic skills, a neophyte, unconsciously driven to personal growth through music and only beginning to discover the world of upscale audio equipment, can go straight from a "sinking ship" to the "vampire's ball."

For this reason, today's increasingly articulated demand for *mindfulness* — especially from the younger generation — requires High End Audio to be completely open when stating its nature.

High End Audio is, first and foremost, a value system, and an approach to the role and responsibility of the listener him/herself. Using the analogy with delicately tuned loudspeaker systems we can call it *active*. A magnificent instrument in unskilled hands sounds no better than what its owner allows for. It is perfectly clear that the attainment of exceptional results requires a clear understanding of the goals set and technical means available. Thus, for High End Audio to continue to be of value for a new generation of audiophiles, it must give relevant, clear, and comprehensible answers to a range of focal questions. This book is dedicated to the author's own answers to those questions.

First of all, we have to consider the main reasons for our fascination with *sound quality*.

- Where does *the struggle for sound quality* during the four ages[2] of audio's development stem from, and what does it entail?

---

[2] If, as an assumption, we mean respectively: the *acoustic, electric, magnetic* and *digital* ages.

- What principles lie at its foundation?

- What are the "low", "medium" and "high" limits of sound quality?

- What does the functionality of High End Audio really mean and what special human needs can we satisfy with — and only with — the help of such special audio equipment?

- What really determines the level of sound quality?

- How are we to move higher and higher towards the absolute "high limit" and what can interfere with that?

- Does money really "talk" in high-performance audio and what are *the true economics of sound quality*?

- Why has High End Audio been in a deep systemic crisis for many years, and what can get it out of its current predicament?

High End Audio can be dissected using entirely different levels of consideration and approaches: consider the molecular structure of the speaker's membranes or the properties of the lacquer used for insulating conductors, for instance. It can be analyzed through the lens of market confrontations and marketing ploys, or engineering insights, audiological research and psychoacoustic principles. Or it can be studied under the light of mythology, fashion, aesthetic theories, semiotics, language construction, anthropology, politics... All of these are valid approaches. But no matter how much we untangle the notorious audiophile wires, gradually, one after the other, at the center of all the nodes of this web we finally discover what is most important: *ourselves*.

The fact that the point of intersection of all the power lines, all the conflicts and the processes is ultimately the listener him/herself can be treated with varying degrees of enthusiasm. Personally, I see both some causes for a cautious optimism and some reasons for a well-founded pessimism — all of these motives actually lie on the same plane. As they say, *"you can't get a good deal from a bad guy"*, especially if that "bad guy" is staring at you every day from a mirror.

Today's world, where the upper bounds of success are sometimes proportional not to the benefits one brings to society but to the harm that one inflicts upon it (an example of a truly systemic malfunction), leaves less and less room for "our soul's elation". It becomes clear in spite of all of the contemporary widespread super-positive business dogmas: if one does not separate morality from business from the onset, one won't get very far. It is precisely for this reason that my pessimism for the immediate future of High End Audio is entirely justified. It is for this very reason the colossal opportunities for widespread use of audio equipment of the highest quality in the first quarter of the 21st century fizzled out in the almost all-encompassing crisis of this industry, the roots of which go back to all of the contradictions the industry has accumulated over the years.

Nevertheless, everything in this world is cyclical — as I've had the opportunity to see in my lifetime in the former USSR — which is what my cautious optimism is built upon.

This book is my contribution to the optimistic scenario in which High End Audio manages to carry the entirety of its value system and its true nature across the abyss of the crisis from the shores of a bright past to a brave new world of the technologically, economically and culturally relevant context of the near future.

This same mission of passing the High End Audio`s torch from the old generation of audiophiles to the new one, determines the direction of my portable High End Audio manufacturing companys *StereoPravda*`s technical development — hopefully — to set an example of how to build a bridge over the gap which would allow this transition to occur.

If one agrees that mass-market audio equipment under the widely known term *hi-fi* and some mysterious hardware of the High End Audio kind are not the same but are actually two different product classes (which we will discuss at length), then the set of quality criteria within each class also has to be distinctly different.

Debunking the view of High End Audio as merely a luxury segment of the home music equipment market in which super expensive hardware plays the role of no more than a mere status symbol, we arrive at the conclusion: the main characteristics of this equipment have to be intrinsically linked with resolutely clear notions of what constitutes the coveted "High Limit of Sound Quality" and which conceptual axioms it rests upon.

Nevertheless, in spite of the fundamental groundwork of the audiophile's ideology formulated in the 1970s and 1980s, its practical use has always been a fairly contentious issue both within the audiophile community and beyond.

Initially creating High End's conceptual structure such disciples as **Harry Pearson**, **J. Gordon Holt** and, among significant others (*sic!*), **Harvey "Gizmo" Rosenberg** (who routinely wore kilt), were almost antipodes. They represented varying and hardly compatible psychotypes, ways of life and mentalities. The academic aesthete Pearson, the technocratic engineer Holt, and the guru of audio shamanism Rosenberg, despite their unquestionably high authority, each pulled the cart of High-End-Audio in seemingly very different directions.

Ironically, it was on ignited subjectivist contradictions within the audiophile community, especially the ones concerning the most precise wording and sound quality criteria, that large Japanese corporations built their main marketing positions in the 60s and 70s. They began to successfully capture markets by employing specific, very precisely formulated and ostensibly "objective" sound quality measurement methods via the use of some corresponding sets of technical specifications. These methods were intended to unequivocally convince the customer that they were directly correlated with the main manifestations of the highest sound quality. It seemed possible therefore to select audio equipment of the "highest quality" by following these criteria to the letter — with these large corporations then adapting their products to these criteria.

In opposition to the Japanese cookie-cutter equipment of the time, the nascent Hight End Audio industry erected its position and navigated the contradictions between what was "good" and "bad" with regard to sound quality by offering alternative subjective methods for evaluating it.

Naturally, both fully objective and a fully subjective approaches are vulnerable, each in its own way.

Without digressing into the vulnerability of the position of large transnational corporations I will just say that in its subsequent development the High End Audio industry was immediately faced with the flip side of its ideologically fundamental (militant) subjectivism. Despite the aforementioned key tenets of the audiophile ideology, formulated under the auspices of *Stereophile* and *The Absolute Sound* magazines, the private interests of its participants contributed to the emergence of violent contradictions in the assessment of the sonic characteristics of specific technologies, audio components or whole audio systems.

Regrettably, a final resolution of these internal contradictions has been constantly hindered by historical, technological and conceptual causes.

In this book we will have to navigate the narrow path between the Scylla of indiscriminate devaluation and the Charybdis of hallucinatory wonder, between dead stereotypes and the cheap exaltation of proselytes, between the skepticism of scientifically-inclined technocrats and the trustworthiness of the "literati" who lack technical knowledge. Across the minefield of the overlaps between equipment design and manufacturing, sound engineering, journalism, sales barricades, music creation and of course the listeners' passionate pursuits we will follow the thorny path of StereoPravda[3].

Beyond the multitude of myths awaits the true essence and real achievements of High End Audio providing enormous opportunities for the well-prepared listener.

Many ideas in this book fully coherent with the results of various academic developments in the second half of the 20th century, namely a return of cultural researchers to the idea that the entirety of human experience can't be divided into parts, as well as with the studies of the media's social role.

Philosopher and culture historian Hans Ulrich Gumbrecht said about his generation which began to look for the new paths in the early 70s:

"Most of all, we were preoccupied with the question of how various means — 'material factors' — of communication have an impact on the meanings that are being transmitted by them. We no

---

[3] The word "*stereo*" stands for "solid" in Greek (e.g. "stereotype"), while the word "*pravda*" is Russian for "truth."

longer believed that the range of meanings could be separated from its 'mediality.' " [4]

Gumbrecht defined aesthetic experience as the oscillation (and occasionally the interference) between what he called the Presence Effect and the Meaning Effect. Placing our subject matter within this context we can ponder the ways in which the listener's "presence" quality (provided by high-end audio systems) correlates with the quality of the "meaning" that is transmitted to him/her, simply put — with the world of music that is increasingly revealed to us with its help.

Ludwig Wittgenstein expressed this in his usual pointed manner in *Tractatus Logico-Philosophicus*:

"A phonograph record, a musical theme, musical notation, sound waves — all of these are in the same state of internal reflection that exists between language and the world. They all have a common logical structure." [5]

I do not have anything against the commonly accepted wording of High End Audio's mission statement which, in the words of the famed sound engineer **Mark Waldrep**, lies in "relaying the accuracy and maximal transmission of the artist's musical intent with no distortions, sound coloration or any other effects, worsening their initial quality" (this quote is translated from Russian).

Nevertheless, the ultimate goal that we must pursue needs to be justified, as do those intentions that can increase our resolve, with the purpose of using such criteria for assessing audio equipment's sound quality and the aesthetic experience of using it.

By way of such justification I will put it as follows: Looking back at my 30-year-long journey in audio and retrospectively assessing what has been its most important part to me throughout all these

---

[4] H.U. Gumbrecht. *Production of Presence: What Meaning Cannot Convey (translated from Russian)*.

[5] L. Wittgenstein. *Tractatus Logico-Philosophicus*. 4.014. *(translated from Russian)*

years, I am convinced again and again that High End Audio has always been *an assortment of the most effective technical instruments for the exhaustive and deepest comprehension of musical languages that are still foreign or new to the tempted listener.* Languages that allow him/her to open new semantic depths in increasingly novel, unfamiliar and — difficult to traverse at first — musical spaces.

However, first things first.

PART

1

Chapter 1. Stereo

How one stops seeing the forest for the trees...?

For years now I've been asking my colleagues in the stereo industry the same tricky question: "What is the original meaning of the word 'stereo'?"

Again and again without fail it is met with a perplexed look: "What do you mean?" I repeat my question: "What does 'stereo' mean?"

Amazingly, during my many years of asking audio equipment manufacturers, their distributors, specialized journalists, sound engineers, musicians and of course regular customers only a handful of them were able to come up with the correct answer...

The subjects of my inquiry are either totally perplexed or (which usually happens) use the following very popular but still incorrect logic: if "mono" means "one" (meaning the number of sound channels), the "stereo" must therefore mean "two", right?

No, not at all.

In fact, the Greek word means "solid", "tangible", "clear" (think, for example, of the familiar word "stereotype").

The reason *Western Electric* chose the word to describe its nascent cinema sound system technology in 1927, and **Alan Blumlein** later picked it up in 1931 as a key word for his patented recording and sound reproduction process was that it reflected their chief purpose: *creating an illusion of a tangible "sound stage" for the listener, made up of "solid", i.e. sharply focused and distinctly spatially localized sound images.*

As the name itself suggests (not to mention the original intent), this fundamental ability of stereo systems to create "solid", i.e. fully palpable to our sonic imagination, clearly localized and well-defined musical images within a sound field (known as the "sound stage"), should be viewed as the key criterion for determining their quality.

Today — almost a hundred years later — Blumlein's fundamental "stereo" technique remains virtually unrivalled in the global music distribution market (and even the latest variations in multichannel sound technology can be viewed merely as a logical development of those same original ideas).

Albeit nowadays colored with bright shades of new design ideas and rapidly developing ancillary technologies, the good old stereo, virtually unchanged over the last century, is still at the heart of the commonly used methods of listening to music. To this day this technology essentially remains the most widespread principle of recording and playing music.

What does this paradoxical deafness to the very name and idea that professionals and consumers have constantly dealt with since time immemorial tell us?

ILLUSTRATION #1
OR "WHY DID THE SOVIET UNION FALL APART?"

After my favorite question about the origins of the word "stereo", I usually continue the conversation with an old joke about why the Soviet Union fell apart.

"Due to the need for secrecy a CIA officer has no idea what his colleagues in the office next door are up to. A British MI6 officer does not know what someone at the desk next to him is doing. And a KGB officer, due to the all-pervading secrecy of the organization, is totally clueless as to what he himself is working on."

Unfortunately, in the similar vein the audio industry, having forgotten some of its most fundamental ideas, has gradually lost sight of its guiding principle — as the famous saying goes, it has "stopped seeing the forest for the trees".

Its many participants, even at the highest levels, have somehow forgotten that the list of criteria used to assess the quality of audio technology — in other words, the set of laws we must follow before we reach our verdict — must not contradict the fundamental Stereo Sound Constitution, originally adopted as the very essence of stereo systems.

Correspondingly, the stereo industry's prospects for the future may be similar to that of the Soviet Union which eventually sunk into oblivion.

Unquestionably, this dilution of focus both during designing and manufacturing of audio products and their promotion as well as when assessing the quality of sound during audio system's testing and installation has far-reaching consequences.

Despite the fact that the latest multichannel recording technology and spatial emulation really do possess far greater possibilities for reproducing a realistic, multidimensional sound field than traditional dual channel stereo its applications remain — particularly in the case of portable audio technology — so limited that, from a practical perspective, it remains a thing of the distant future rather than the present.

At the same time ways to achieve the secondary — in terms of their effect on overall quality parameters of audio equipment — characteristics: timbre, frequency extension, overall loudness dynamic range, amounts of distortions of all kinds, etc., which the media (usually affiliated with mass-market manufacturers of electronic equipment) usually focuses on should really only be used as supporting tools for recreating and supplementing (or, embellishing) the fundamental stereo effect. Actually, only after the demonstration of this effect of three-dimensionality of stereo musical reproduction or, in other words, sound "holography" is maximized should reasonable attention be given to the system's other sonic parameters...

Thus the demonstrated degree of the primary holography effect of musical reproduction — the Holy Grail of the stereo industry — is, according to the initial designation of this technology, the main criterion for assessing the quality of audio systems of the highest caliber.

In the Land of the Deaf

In reality all of us are, to various extents, hard of hearing. We mostly remain on the plane of the averaged and unconscious auditory experience, experiencing neither peaks nor valleys. Both "averaged" and "unconscious" should be emphasized.

So often do our capabilities fall drastically short of our desires... Beginning with the earliest experiments in sound recording and reproduction man has been driven by a particular dynamic trying to attain the thousand-year-old Utopia of the "music of the spheres" which at a certain point moved to the *pure sound* register. The very word "utopia" (meaning something that "has no place", does not exist), infallibly beckons and invites to search for the cherished goal. The motives of audiophiles reflect a certain Pythagoreanism in which "absolute" music is replaced with "absolute" sound.

Back in the 18th century, long before the sound recording revolution, a curios idea existed that the voice of a vocally gifted artist could be preserved by blowing air through his severed head and employing lever-driven sound-producing apparatus[1]. Edison was obsessed with the idea of a "spirit phone" — a device that could be used to contact the world of the dead — while Tesla was developing a "spirit radio" and even believed to have caught the right wavelength once.

John Cage was into the idea of hearing mushrooms, Xenakis and Stockhausen believed in sound's ability to generate architectural structures and the synthesizer's creator, Peter Zinoviev, has long given up on manually-controlled systems, believing that the future of music lies in a direct interaction between mind and sound with no intermediaries.

The flip side of this dream — separation of sound and music — can lead to the loss of the subordinate nature inherent in their

---

[1] What I wouldn't give to see that!

relationship. This inevitably leads to all kinds of glitches in the delivery of music from the "transmitter" to the "receiver" — when, enthralled with Sound, audiophiles stop hearing the Music.

Thus, as they say, "to each his own madness", and "deaf" audiophiles that have lost their connection to music are far from alone in that.

The examples above show how dangerous and demanding the games that humanity keeps getting itself into really are. We cannot escape the fact that the ideology of the *absolute sound* has to be complemented with the ideology of *the absolute listener*. But where does one find such a listener? For him or her to be able to hear and listen they need to first become familiar with the appropriate system of coordinates.

In pursuit of yet another Utopia instead of finding solid ground and beginning from scratch many lose the ability to acknowledge and value real achievements and also cease to understand the real processes and validated principles. They keep on trying to upgrade the same old rusty bicycle that won't take them very far no matter how much they try.

ILLUSTRATION #2
OR DAVID CRONENBERG'S *STEREO*

David Cronenberg's first film, *Stereo*, made in 1969, has a unique take on a situation in which our limitless intentions meet the limitations of our receptors.

The film's events take place at a mysterious research facility in the not too distant future (possibly our present). A group of people is subjected to experiments aimed at uncovering extra sensual perception and communication abilities — with telepathy implied to be the main one, naturally.

The world in which the test subjects gradually have their speech, auditory and other sensory centers removed is submerged in absolute silence, there is an atmosphere of nearly intolerable deprivation. Sometimes voiceover text, excerpts from bizarre research reports and test results[2] that mention the mysterious doctor Luther Stringfellow, whom we never actually meet, is read over the action that is robbed of its sound.

The story's outcome is a sad one — many of the subjects lose their minds or become emotionally unhinged and hyper aggressive[3]...

The "deaf spot" in our hearing appears to me far more elusive than the "blind spot" in our vision. As a result of an

---

[2] Often reminiscent of the technical jargon of audio publications and Internet audio forums...

[3] How not to be reminded of the unfortunate audiophiles with their endless battles?

especially deep location of our auditory centers and their proximity to the subconscious even the conceptualization of auditory — and hence musical — reality presents an incredibly challenging task, it is often difficult or even utterly impossible to choose the right words for it. When talking about music and sound we are constantly drowning, slipping as if in a dream. It is not by accident that the human ear contains traces and functionality of the so-called "lateral line", used by our oldest ancestors — fish — for orientation in space. Through evolution the lateral line was transformed into the vestibular apparatus which is why the ear also remains the organ of balance.

It is the ear that is often home to the mystical (or pseudo mystical) experiences. And it is no accident that while trying to rule out psychosis, doctors meticulously check whether their patients hear "voices".

It is useful to keep in mind that the man who has the honor of inventing the very term "High End Audio", the founder of American magazine *The Absolute Sound*, Harry Pearson, viewed the concept of that very "Absolute Sound", for the reproduction of which high-end equipment is made, as *the attainment of the maximum possible conformity between the sound of the recording that is being played and the corresponding original sound of real acoustic instruments played live within natural acoustic space*. Nothing more, nothing less.

In this case, the role of reference point and sonic ideal is assumed by, for instance, the sound of a live symphonic orchestra in an appropriate concert hall. Yet a philharmonic auditory experience has not been formative for the last several generations of listeners. John Cage complained about it: "It is sad that the times of every house having a piano and almost all members of the family playing it have passed. They now listen to the radio or watch TV." [4] Today, when bothersome and largely synthetic signals are broadcast "from every orifice", given a noise-polluted urban space and an endless stream of information, the factors that shape our day-to-day auditory experience are very different from those even in the early 70s when Pearson was creating his magazine.

Yet the dramatic struggle for sound quality which began in the middle of the 19th century and continues to this day in the digital age is also usually left without common people's attention. Finding themselves on a plateau, they are rarely exposed to the truly *low* sound limits, which our ancestors began with, and hardly have any idea of the *high* limit which they could strive for...

[4] Richard Kostelyanets. *Conversations with Cage (translated from Russian)*.

Between Technology and Art – A Balancing Act

Actually, the abundance of broken spears around the sonic Holy Grail is explained by a simple reason. Historically, pure audio was the oldest domain of consumer electronics and it was the period before World War Two — after which the development focus irrevocably shifted to video and television[5] — that became the "golden age" of the development of all the core audio technologies (with the exception of digital ones).

In addition, as drastic improvements in sound quality occurred in the 1930s and 1940s, neither the knowledge in this domain, nor the available measurement tools of that time allowed to formulate any sets of procedures or design equipment for creating exhaustive and comprehensive standards for sound quality. In this respect a set of conditions to develop and adopt commonly accepted quality standards for video images proved more fortunate as merely a couple of decades later such scientific and technological conditions for video equipment were fully formed — which became the main reason for its subsequent explosive development.

The commonly accepted standards for sound quality however remained unformulated which allows to this day (!) to interpret them liberally depending on, for example, specific methods of promoting audio equipment or a particular context of its application.

As a result the initially "garage-based" High End Audio industry finding itself at the very peak of sonic achievements exists in a space resembling something of a *fold* — meaning it is located at the intersection of technology and art where objective technical

---

[5] Thus, the saying that, in terms of sound quality, *"the future of audio is in the past"* (meaning that the average sound quality of "old" equipment may be much higher than of the one made today) remains relevant to this day.

aspects are merely a set of instruments for the creation of auditory art — impossible to measure, and the quality of which can only be assessed subjectively. As with any art form, this allows the human factor to take center stage while it would never have occurred to the well-known large corporations and the biggest audio equipment manufacturers, to step from a purely objective system of assessing their product's sound quality to such shaky ground as an arbitrary set of subjective judgements of some alleged "audio experts."

Thus the closest analogy for upscale audio equipment is provided by custom, exclusive, hand-crafted *musical instruments*: that is, when there is unquestionably room for "technology" (moreover, of the most precise and delicate kind) in their production, but their quality assessment may rest not on abstract technical measurements, but on purely subjective judgements by experts possessing all the appropriate (including auditioning) skills.

Given a lack of a commonly accepted rigid system of sound quality standards, this dichotomy between *objective technical indicators* and *subjective perception effects* to a great extent forms the fundamental core of the conflict within the industry. However, this basic conflict reveals a multitude of derivatives, eluding our attention behind the ghosts of imaginary contradictions and false alternatives, like the holy wars between "the analog" and "the digital", "tubes" and "transistors", "horn-loaded" and "planar" loudspeakers, as well as between "professional" and "home" audio.

The methodology of High End Audio lies in the fact that only actual (i.e. "subjective") auditioning of stereo equipment allows to ultimately judge its sonic qualities: as, in fact, no technical instruments except out ears (more precisely — our brains) still exist for the assessment of the degree of the three-dimensional "holography" of the sound stage it produces.

If we accept "holography" of reproduced sound as the basis for sound quality assessment when designing, manufacturing, promoting, installing and finally listening to audio equipment (which, by the way, is fully in line with Harry Pearson's tenets), we can responsibly proclaim the following: *true High End Audio with its methodology of audio systems' design and production as well as their sound quality's assessment is, in essence, a return to the very roots of the original technology known as "stereo"*. This definition of the main sound quality criterion contains an explanation as to why the objectivist shift of sonic priorities undergone by mass market equipment manufacturers represents a *substitution of the primary with the secondary*. This biased and limited one-sidedness of judgement also contains the main reason why, in terms of original stereo sound, any audio products that rely exclusively on an objective set of measurements — which are still fully incapable of determining the degree of sonic holography manifestation effect — with regards to their sonic qualities are, by definition, inferior.

One can use relatively trivial methods to affect sonic aspects of lesser significance than sound "holography". For instance, a manufacturer can easily change the timbre "coloration" of his products with a simple "boost" or "roll off" of high or low frequencies; or, let's say, with relatively simple manipulations of circuitry it is able to either "open up" or "constrict" sonic "micro dynamics" liveliness in the sound signature of its equipment — and so forth. Thus the explanation of such persistent attempts by manufacturers of mass-produced equipment to divert the public's attention from the primary aspects of equipment sound quality to secondary ones is a very simple one.

From a technical standpoint, focusing on relatively accurate sound coloration, its sonic dynamic properties, minimal distortion levels and so forth is a path of *least* resistance, whereas the task of creating a sufficiently pronounced stereo effect requires the use of far more thorough, elaborate and therefore expensive production methods and techniques — for both the design and manufacturing of audio equipment (let alone additional complexity of its proper installation).

Accordingly, as the fundamental attribute of stereo systems — creating "holographic" sound — is also the most difficult to attain, mass-market equipment manufacturers are ever so keen to shift the public's attention from this key property to indirect, secondary features — thus replacing the original version of this technology with its surrogate.

In terms of High End Audio these secondary aspects of sound quality simply need to be "honed" and then accurately and coherently (that is, in time domain) matched with each other during each of the specific stage of a concrete audio equipment design, manufacturing and installation. While any manifestation of a subjectively remarkable "holography" effect is always the proof that these secondary instrumental aspects of audio performance have assumed (once again, not generally speaking, but for this given case) their optimal values and are fully in sync with one another.

The converse, in turn, is not true: some broad objective notions on some generalized *ideal* parameters of secondary sound quality manifestations (such as its timbre, dynamics, distortion levels, even perfect phase coherence behavior of each separate component and so on) will never allow to make (especially for a specific audio system) any even slightly realistic predictions regarding the potential levels of "holography" reproduction, i.e. the most meaningful "stereo" effect.

A direct analogy can be made here with the capture and reproduction of photo and video images.

Following this analogy, in theory, to attain the maximum sound "focusing" in any given instance and in a given space, home stereo systems should supposedly provide access to a sufficient set of sound adjustment capabilities (as is the case, for instance, with the focus settings for photo and video cameras or projectors).

On the contrary, a complete lack of such adjustment capabilities "aboard" the vast majority of audio equipment made today (moreover, even of the most expensive and "advanced" kind) is nothing if not the proof of a regrettable trend. Namely that not only mass-market, but even the most upscale segments of the audio industry, have gradually forgotten their beginnings and have completely stopped seeing the forest of principal ideas that lie at their foundation behind the trees of secondary particularities of a much pettier kind...

Chapter 2. The Struggle for Sound Quality

A BRIEF HISTORICAL OVERVIEW

Utopia

The audiophile Utopia like everything related to human senses and limits of perception is in many ways rooted in the Platonic Cave. Moreover, it is for the sonic dimension that this famous metaphor is perhaps most accurate, considering how the goals, pursued by designers of audio recording and reproduction chains while perfecting their systems and processes, have been understood throughout history...

ILLUSTRATION #3
OR *The Myth of the Cave*

In the 7th book of the *Republic* Plato paints this legendary scene. For almost literal description of a background shared by audio equipment manufacturers and consumers, it would suffice to simply replace the verb *"see"* with the verb *"hear"*.

<...> "See human beings as though they were in an underground cave-like dwelling with its entrance, a long one, open to the light across the whole width of the cave. They are in it from childhood with their legs and necks in bonds so they are fixed, seeing only in front of them, unable because of the bond to turn their heads all the way around. Their light is from a fire burning far above and behind them. Between the fire and the prisoners there is a road above, along which see a wall, built like the partitions puppet-handlers set to hide their assistants and above which they show the puppets."

"I see," Glaucon said.

"Then also see along this wall some people carrying all sorts of utensils, which they hold the way that you can see the things — including statues of animals wrought from stone, wood and every kind of material — above the wall; as is to be expected, some of them talk with each other while others are silent."

"It is a strange picture and strange prisoners you're telling of!"

"They're like us. To start with, do you suppose such men would have seen anything of themselves and one another besides the shadows cast by the fire on the side of the cave facing them?"

"How could they, if they had been compelled to keep their heads motionless throughout their life?"

"And what about the things that are carried by? Isn't it the same with them?"

"Meaning?"

"If the prisoners were able to discuss things with one another, don't you believe they would hold that they are naming these things going by before them that they see?"

"Definitely."

<...> "Take a man who is released and compelled to stand up, to turn his neck around, to walk and look up toward the light; and who, moreover, in doing all this is in pain and, because he is dazzled, is unable to make out those things whose shadows he saw before. What do you suppose he'd say if someone were to tell him that before he saw silly nothings, while now, because he is somewhat nearer to what *is* and more turned toward beings, he sees more correctly; and, in particular, showing him each of the things that pass by, were to compel the man to answer his questions about what they are? Don't you suppose he'd be at a loss and believe that what was seen before is truer than what is now shown?"

"Yes, by far."

"And, if compelled to look at the light itself, would his eyes hurt and would he flee, turning away to those things that he is able to make out and hold them to be really clearer than what is being shown?"

"So he would."

Besides everything else, Plato reminds us of the fate awaiting the *media*. While providing access to reality, the media simultaneously become an insurmountable obstacle on the path towards fully comprehending the truth.

Throughout the history of these twin brothers — *sound recording* and *sound reproduction* — each new technological stage has activated the strive to minimize the effects of intermediaries between music and listener — in other words, making them as transparent as possible.

From this the eternal paradox for hard core audiophiles arises: as the level of technical sophistication of all intermediary elements of a sound system increases, so does the length and complexity of the audio signal flow path; at the same time every component of the audio system performing its function within the bigger picture has to be perfected in such a way so as to minimize the manifestation of its presence in this chain. Thus, on the one hand, the final sound quality has to be *inversely proportional* to signal flow path complexity, on the other — the quality of its elements is *proportional* to their capacity for transmitting the source signal with no distortions, letting it pass through without adding or subtracting anything.

The principle of moving the upper boundary, a gradual approach to seeing a full picture, to purity, to transparency and, finally, to what is often referred to among audiophiles as the *equipment disappearance effect* or the *palpability effect* — it is actually the dream that one day we will stop hearing from behind a curtain and meet the Truth. Its irresistible pull has been present since the very inception of the audio industry and has been its guiding light at all times.

But even here, breaking free of the chains and heading towards the exit from the "cave", one must remember Plato's warning.

Returning from the realm of Utopia to the ground, one must note that, on par with this conceptual and technological determination, which will initially find its laconic expression in the *high fidelity* formula, a trend for a compromise, more bland and mundane approach to audio equipment has been developing. Secondary sonic characteristics will become key and fundamental for such an approach, getting boiled down not to how the equipment *sounds*, but to how easily and conveniently it fits within various lifestyle scenarios, how well it looks in the living room as well as to what extent the specifics of its design allow for inexpensive and widespread distribution. For the most part it was this second trend that has determined the audio climate within which audio equipment industry at large has developed.

The evolution of audio systems has always gone hand in hand with the evolution of those listeners who, on the one hand, used them, on the other, through a feedback loop, got locked down within the sonic landscape that gear generated.

A listener in Edison's time differs even from those of Berliner's era, let alone our contemporaries. Value and aesthetic signposts at every historical stage, while directing engineering and scientific developments, were at the same time limited by the current capabilities. Besides, both have always felt the considerable pressure of the market forces. Accordingly, at every stage of audio's development *Aesthetics*, *Technology* and *Business* formed a triangle of extremely entangled relationships.

Illustration #4

or The Low Limit of Sound

When Édouard-Léon Scott de Martinville was developing the *first ever* audio recording device in the middle of the 19th century he could not even count on even *hearing* the result of his hard work.

The song "Au Clair de la Lune", sung by Scott into the horn of a *Phonautograph* he invented in 1857 was only found in a Parisian archive and replayed in 2008. As has been proven by now, it is the first audio recording in history. One is justified to say that it is the historical "lower limit of sound".

For a hundred and fifty years the recording remained mute, to be looked at only. Today the experience of listening to the firstborn of audio recording is in many ways akin to looking at the first ever photograph taken by Joseph Nicéphore Niépce in 1827.

We can discern what Scott is singing on the recording about as well as we can distinguish the details of the landscape seen through the window on the first photograph in history.

We can almost *hear* the soot which covered the manually rotated glass cylinder of the device. The unevenness of the needle's movements, the creaking and rustling against the surface covered in grime, a background that devours the figure again and again, the hissing through which a heavily distorted signal vaguely resembling a human crying is barely discernible[1].

---

[1] It is noteworthy that, at first, it appeared to the researchers that the recorded voice belonged to a child or woman. It was later discovered that the playback speed was accelerated, and the voice recorded is that of Scott.

While one can look at the first photograph today with curiosity and even discern the image, the first audio recording, only ten seconds long, is capable of inflicting veritable suffering on a modern listener.

The phonautograph's "Moonlight", like an uncertain and strained yet hopeful crying of a newborn, reaching us one and a half centuries later, serves as the starting point of the long and constant *struggle for sound quality* that began at the end of the 19th century and continued throughout the entirety of the 20th.

That fight began with the first efforts that made the recording of live sounds *possible*. Having invented and patented his *Phonograph* in 1877, **Thomas Edison** did not stop there but continued to perfect various elements of the device.

The fundamental mechanical principle according to which *sound vibrations, passing through the acoustic horn, cause a membrane to vibrate, which in turn transmits the vibrations to a needle, leaving a trace (the groove) on the sound recording layer of the revolving cylinder* will stay fundamental through the whole acoustic era of audio up until the dawn of the age of electricity: the spread of the condenser microphone and the triode amplifier in the 1920s.

Raising the sound quality of recording and playback chains will become the principal motivation from the beginning on par with the breadth of the corresponding technologies' distribution and the development of new audio applications.

Signal transmission and all of its characteristics required improvement (first and foremost — the resulting *absolute loudness* and *reproduced frequency range*). Besides, the problems of *longevity* and *replicability* of the storage medium had to be solved, and the *playback length* to be increased. Accordingly, all of the fundamental and intrinsically linked initial developments in the realm of audio technologies can be divided into two classes:

a. Sound recording and playback equipment;
b. Recording storage medium.

Edison's phonograph as an embryo already contains many of the elements of all future audio chains including those that define the most complicated audio systems of the modern age. All the principal thresholds that an audio signal passes remain unchanged to this day.

Leaving all the details of the historical development of sound recording technology as well as radio and television transmissions of the recordings aside, the evolution of distinct component classes of audio systems can be represented with DIAGRAM 1 (see next page).

Whichever of the widespread periodization systems we choose — the one that divides the history of audio into two main stages (*acoustic and electric* or *analog and digital*) or the one that adds *magnetic* as a stage in itself — we will see that, while the key elements of the audio signal flow path were transformed, changed their shape, design, etc., during evolutionary stages that relied on increasingly sophisticated technologies and newly discovered physical theories which were opening new horizons for improvement, in essence those elements' core sonic functionality stayed the same.

Starting at the very *lowest limit of sound* and slowly moving higher and higher towards baseline sound quality that we now take for granted and which we currently habitually use for gauging it (even if that average evaluation would yield us an equivalent of "an average body temperature in a hospital, including morgue") audio equipment designers completed a journey that is now over a century and a half long.

It's noteworthy that the principal role in the desired improvements of audio in its early stages was played by *speech reproduction*, the naturalness of the transmission of which was the main criterion of assessing sound quality, while human *voice* was initially the primary musical instrument. This appropriately parallels the newest developments in sound holography recreation

	Cylinder	Phonograph record				Magnetic wire/tape	Optical disc	Digital file	
MEDIUM	Cylinder	Phonograph record				Magnetic wire/tape	Optical disc	Digital file	
DELIVERY	Phonoautograph (1857)	Phonograph (1877)	Gramophone (1887)	Pathephone (1913)	Electric player (late 1920s)	Tape recorder (1935)	Laser player (1978)	Software digital audio player (1997)	Streamers (2006)
DELIVERY TRANSMISSION	Manual		Automatic		Electric			Software	
READER	Acoustic pickup ("needle")				Electric pickup ("needle")	Magnetic head	Laser head	File reading software	
AMPLIFIER	—	Acoustic horn			Tube amplifier			Transistor amplifier / Class D amplifier	
ACOUSTIC SYSTEMS	—	Acoustic horn		Horn, concealed inside system chassis	Electrodynamic loudspeaker	Modern horn / dynamic / electrostatic / plasma / planar loudspeakers			

ANALOG AGE   DIGITAL AGE

[DIAGRAM 1]

technologies that are aimed at increasing the efficiency of foreign language learning (more on that later).

That's why at the historic demonstration for the US President among a list of ten applications in which Edison defined the purpose of his invention music was almost last — behind letter dictation, books for the blind, precise time service, oratory, speech culture and foreign language learning.

In its early days, the phonograph did not record the [sh] sound, and separate sounds — such as [d] and [t] — sounded the same. Due to similar articulatory defects it will later become apparent — with the invention of the gramophone and a wider spread of sound recording — that, for example, the sound of a bass drum is almost impossible to reproduce with this technology, which is why it will be replaced with a woodblock for orchestra recordings. Singers with loud, clear voices, brass wind instruments such as the trumpet and the trombone will do well while others will be left behind. For instance, the guitar will lose the competition to the banjo which always sounded brighter on early recordings.

All of this should remind us of the principal non-linear effect that the complete sound recorder/transmitter chain can have on the contents of the message, with its special characteristics fully determining the musical tastes, style and new contexts for music's existence.

For a long time the instruments that were producing a wide range of frequencies (especially low) are simply left out off the menu of audio recording options. Although it will later be possible to expand the bandwidth of first-generation records — nevertheless throughout the entire acoustic age sound quality will remain exceptionally low, only reproducing sound frequencies not lower than 250 Hz and not higher than 2500 Hz[2].

---

[2] Compare this with today's typical reproduction frequency bandwidth of around 30 — 16 000 Hz.

A constant urge to improve sound quality will motivate audio designers to look for the new ways, time and time again.

Finally Edison, experimenting with the materials and sound storage medium design, will replace the foil coating with a solid wax cylinder from which grooves that have previously been recorded can be easily removed. Employing a diamond needle for recording, he will achieve an increase in sound quality and will slightly extend playback time.

However, the sound that is reproduced from wax cylinders will be much quieter than that of the earlier tin ones, which is why they will be listened to through a tube inserted into the ear akin to a stethoscope — proving to be a significant limitation of this technology.

At first every recording was produced individually: a single two-minute song was simultaneously recorded with ten phonographs and after that new cylinders would be installed and a new recording made. This procedure had to be completed up to fifty times every single day. Later, attempts were made to acoustically re-record from one cylinder to the others.

The lack of a convenient method of replicating cylinders became the main reason that limited the spread of Edison's pioneering technology.

In 1887, i.e. ten years after Edison received the patent for the phonograph, **Emile Berliner** patented the *Gramophone*. The main innovation in Berliner's invention was that instead of the rapidly disintegrating wax cylinders of a phonograph — which was already widespread as a voice recorder by that time — one could now produce easily replicable and convenient flat plates that contained both purely recreational and serious artistic recordings. Constantly improved, it is this technology that will dominate audio for most of the 20th century.

In the 1910s the gramophone record will leave all of its many competitors behind in the storage medium format wars, and by the end of the 1920s Edison's phonograph medium will disappear entirely, taking its place in the museum of history.

Berliner, having founded *Victor Talking Machine Company* with his partner **Eldridge Johnson,** will thus lay the foundations of the modern audio recording industry.

As public recognition grew, future designs were increasingly dependent on the nascent market demand. What's more, while the patent wars raged, people's needs and tastes have had time to change significantly.

The first type of gramophone was termed *"horn gramophone"* — for the simple reason that it used an acoustic horn as a loudspeaker. The shape, size and material of the horn will change repeatedly. During the heyday of the gramophone's popularity (before the appearance of radio) the range of horns to choose from will be vast, not to satisfy the listeners' needs but mainly existing for the pleasure of housewives, preoccupied with appearance (the proverbial *"wife acceptance factor"*[3]). Experiments will lead to the creation of highly exotic specimen — ones like the "Twin Serpent Horn" which combined two horns in a single snake-like casing for increased volume. Equally extravagant was the system of two isolated pickups (each with its own horn), moving along the record groove with a delay of a fraction of a second, designed to create a "pseudo-stereoscopic" effect.

Later the traditional horn will transform into a horn, *concealed within the system body,* with these models becoming widely known as *pathephones* (1913), so called because they were originally produced by the French firm *Pathé.* Pathephones resembled

---

[3] Also known among audiophiles as the "WAF".

briefcase, were easier to transport and allowed to listen to the music in new, absolutely unexpected before, conditions. Here we are approaching the familiar and most often associated with any audio system shape of a "box".

ELECTRICITY AGE

Despite all these important innovations and mechanical tweaks the principal step forward in the struggle for sound quality was the spread by the mid-20s of household electrical power supply — and, as a result, *condenser microphones* and *tube triode amplifiers*, which, together, have opened heretofore unthought-of possibilities for audio.

The research of **John Ambrose Fleming** and the inventions of **Lee De Forest**, who created the electronic vacuum triode in 1906, were of paramount importance. The appearance of this tube became the foundation of the electronic revolution, to a large extent determined the shape of the whole 20th century. It is De Forest whom radio and television owe their existence to. Finally, after the condenser microphone was invented by a *Bell Labs* engineer **Edward Wente** in 1916, a new age in audio began. United in a single system, a condenser microphone and a triode tube amplifier were capable of ensuring a fundamentally new level of recording and playback sound quality.

Rapid development of electronics followed, and the acoustic method of sound recording was replaced with the electronic one.

In the electronic method of audio recording, *sound vibrations affect the microphone, where they are transformed into corresponding electric waves. The latter's amplitude is amplified by specialized amplifiers to the necessary magnitude, determined by the sensitivity* of the recording equipment. Which then transforms these electric vibrations into the mechanical vibrations of the cutter for cutting the grooves on the master lacquer to be used to produce successive generation stamps to press records.

Unlike the acoustic method of sound recording the invention of the electronic one allowed to reproduce a far greater range of recorded frequencies — from 50 to 10 000 Hz — with much lower levels of amplitude, frequency and other kinds of distortions.

In the first half of the 1920s the whole world will see the development of *radio broadcasting* that transmitted sounds over very long distances. Electronic tube receivers and amplifiers will be used for receiving radio broadcast programs. Even the first dynamic loudspeaker drivers (colloquially known as "drivers") used in radio receivers will demonstrate a better sound quality than the best gramophones — both with exposed and encased horns — of the time. The operational principle of the dynamic speaker driver will be patented by **Chester Rise** and **Edward Kellogg** in 1924.

The design of the first electrodynamic loudspeakers featured high-resistance coils of electric wire which essentially played the role of magnets, bringing the paper or cloth membrane into motion.

Radio made a significant contribution to the sound quality criteria system due to its fundamental principle: *the principle of spatial and polarization selection of radio waves and their transformation into electric radio signals.* Separating the target signal from the multitude of other interfering signals and noises; amplifying and transforming the target signal into a state in which the information it contains becomes usable — implementing these processes shone a new light on the tasks facing the audio industry, which now became concerned with increasing the *sensitivity* of devices as well as meticulously reducing the level of the transmitter's own *noise*, expanding the *dynamic range* — and so on. Thus discoveries and innovations in radio played a defining role in all future developments of audio equipment.

When the drastic decrease of phonograph records sales (as a result of the avalanche-like growth of radio's popularity) began the record itself started to change in response: not only in terms of the material (from shellac to the ultimately adopted vinyl) but also in size, the properties of encoded signal pickup "phono" cartridges as well as discs' rotations-per-minute (RPM) speed. After years of research and experimentation with the RPM speed and density of record grooves, only in 1948 will the so-called vinyl *long play record* (LP) finally be introduced. If in the mid-20s record playback time did not exceed 3–5 minutes per side, it now increased to 20 minutes or more. This meant that only by the end of the 1940s did the first opportunity appear to fit within the space of a single sound carrier a complete piece of, for instance, classical music with no interruptions — which would have previously required a whole stack of phonograph records.

The acoustic-mechanic gramophone has been replaced by the *electrical player*, which is made up of a multitude of mechanisms and electrical circuits necessary for both reading and transmitting information from vinyl records further along the playback chain.

With no built-in amplifier or loudspeakers the electric player got a chance to become the central part of more complex systems — *electrophones* and *radiolas*. The electrophone combined a player, a full amplifier and an acoustic system. The radiola added a radio receiver to the set.

A true breakthrough in the history of sound equipment which served as the main catalyst for the appearance of contemporary High End Audio came with the *stereo* technology, patented by Alan Blumlein back in 1931, but first implemented in a commercial product only in the late 1950s (the first vinyl stereo record was released in 1957).

As with the stereo sound technology itself, the biggest audio achievements of the 1930s came from the film industry. Producers and film directors quickly realized that sound is the "heart and soul" of a film, it helps to convey emotions through music, enhancing dialogue and images, having a deep emotional impact. The "talking" aspect made the tiresome subtitles redundant while the impact of music and sound effects helped create new kinds of movies which moved the audience much more deeply than before.

Almost a hundred years later this is taken for granted but the very fact of combining sound and image created a new environment, the effect of which differs to a surprising extent from the separate effects of its components — musical recordings and silent images.

The film industry came to the conclusion that increasing the fidelity of sound track reproduction (thanks to optical sound, better amplifiers and better loudspeakers) significantly increases the emotional impact of watching a film.

Western Electric (the manufacturing and R&D arm of the telephone systems' manufacturer *Bell Labs*) and the *RCA/NBC* alliance fought over the creation of the highest sound quality possible. In the 1930s the sound of films will become the main concern of the professional audio industry whose most important innovations will inevitably trickle down to the consumer audio market shortly afterwards.

Thus in the span of a decade (1929–1939) the foundations of the modern stereo industry were laid: both of its mass segments — *high fidelity* — and its highest level, later dubbed *High End Audio*. Both the Golden Age of hi-fi in the 50s and the directly heated vacuum triode-based Ultra-Fi equipment movement of the 90s share common roots — the knowledge and ideas formed and developed during that decade.

The works of Blumlein and the research departments of *RCA* and *Western Electric* remind us that in audio we are still standing on the shoulders of those giants. None of the subsequent eras in audio were even remotely comparable in terms of overall significance of their achievements to the 1930s, followed by consolidation and subsequent spread of technology from research laboratories to the homes of the ever growing number of ordinary listeners — at increasingly affordable prices.

Meanwhile, the enormous army of electronic engineers that were discharged from service at the end of WWII, having acquired supreme technical skills during military campaigns, was attempting to apply them to consumer industries upon the return to civil life.

A generational change occurred during this period — the first wave of pioneers passed the torch to audio engineers who will create the Golden Age of high fidelity in the 1950s.

In an interview with me for the Russian *Audiomagazin* in 2007 **John Atkinson**, the editor of the American magazine *Stereophile*, reminisced about the large number of people that were building their own DIY (Do-It-Yourself) home audio kits at the time. These systems were often designed around German trophy tape recorders, the first of which (*AEG Magnetophon K1*) was introduced back in 1935.

The arrival of the *Ampex* open reel-to-reel tape recorder — also based on the captured German *Magnetophon* — became a significant event in the late 1940s. The German *tape biasing* technology was known in the US and Britain before the war but was ignored by the English-speaking world in favor of wire recorders of far more mediocre quality. During the post-war years all the technological issues with the manufacturing of the iron oxide-covered magnetic tape were resolved, and the new *Ampex* tape recorders quickly surpassed the German originals in terms of sound quality. The introduction and fast improvement of *magnetic tape recording* became the prerequisite for the impressive sonic achievements of the 1950s.

At the same time the US broadcasting industry opened hundreds of high quality FM radio stations, Good Music, in the 50s — transmitting classical, jazz and pop music. The era from the early 50s to mid-60s is marked by a musical and sound quality of radio broadcasting that will not be surpassed in the future.

Meanwhile, as the audio signal chain elements became more complex in terms of technology and design, technical requirements for each grew as well, with a later trend towards them becoming the separate components.

However, contrary to the tendency to separate systems into components the market was ever more persistent about the need to package all the parts as economically as possible (both in terms of size and price) while the specialized press, as it usually happens, readily performed the function of servicing mass market equipment manufacturers.

In this way the *audioconsoles* that are already familiar to us from the past got their next lease on life, uniting all the elements of an audio system in a single chassis — from the sound source to built-in loudspeakers. This console configuration remains for the most part the only audio system reference type in the general public's imagination.

But despite the wide distribution of audio consoles of every kind the most passionate enthusiasts continued to perfect separate components in their garages — speakers, amplifiers, phono stage preamplifiers, players, tonearms, pickup phono cartridges and so on.

THE UNCOMPROMISING IDEAL OF ABSOLUTE QUALITY

In 1945 **Paul Klipsch** patented the *Klipschorn* loudspeaker, the arrival of which is viewed by many experts in the field as the starting point in the history of *high fidelity*, or *hi-fi*.

Very much in the spirit of the times Klipsch assembled each loudspeaker by himself — and could only afford to hire an engineer in 1948. He managed to implement the idea — revolutionary at the time — of an acoustic horn that was *folded inside the speaker*. The development of such a horn loaded speaker became the cornerstone of his work. Klipsch was able to make the reverse reflection of sound waves inside the body serve the loudspeaker, thus increasing their efficiency; when calculating the speaker's parameters, Klipsch considered walls and room corners as an extension of the speaker's body. These speakers impressed listeners with the feeling of spaciousness their provided, while their size was far more compact than that of most competitors.

In order to appreciate the breakthrough achieved in loudspeaker design at the time one must realize what the loudspeakers of the late 40s were like. There was no real technical understanding of the properties of systems with "sealed" and "ported" speaker enclosures, and most loudspeakers of the time were hollow-sounding and poorly balanced by today's standards.

Up until the mid-50s engineers worked on fundamental improvements of the electrical speaker driver. Experiments with cone materials, voltage levels and coil designs were conducted. Yet the sound of speakers remained unnatural for a long time, and deep bass reproduction was out of question up until the invention of the *"sealed box"* by **Edgar Villchur** in 1954. The use of a simple — as everything brilliant is — sealed body allowed not only to significantly enrich the sound of loudspeakers with lower frequencies (adding a full-bodied quality to it) but also reduce their size from that of a huge and heavy cabinet to a small *"bookshelf."*

The appearance of a sound storage medium of significantly higher quality in the form of the vinyl stereo record at the end of the 1950s, which has survived almost unchanged to this day, became the point of bifurcation not just for the whole audio industry. It seems that a minimum sound quality threshold exists, above which, as the famous Russian theatre director Stanislavsky would put it, our perception of a performance — in this case, an audio system's performance — switches from the state of "I don't believe it!" to that of "I do believe it!". In other words, it shifts from a mode of full awareness that our imagination is focused solely on *music playback's audio performance* into the mode of skipping over and ignoring the intermediary audio playback stage to refocuse our imagination on the *original musical performance itself* to plunge directly into it.

> The same division leap in provided performance quality was reached at the appearance of the DVD (Digital Video Disc) technology forty years later. While analog video cassettes with fairly low image quality were the primary medium before, the introduction of images of incomparably higher quality with the first consumer digital video formats gave an impetus to a new videophile phenomenon — *High End Video*, which was implemented in a new segment of advanced custom installations of home theatres.

Thus in the late 1950s the quality of the storage medium, coupled with advances in the fields of electronics as well as loudspeaker and vinyl record player design that were already made, brought audio equipment sonic properties very close to fully conforming with the primary properties of the human hearing apparatus (with the exception of a fully realistic recreation of a three-dimensional sonic space which only the most modern multichannel sound systems are capable of reproducing).

These achievements could not fail to turn heads and give a burst of energy for new accomplishments among true audio enthusiast community.

By and large the modern audio industry was born in symbiosis with the source — by then in full swing — of the endless supply of properly recorded and transmitted music of the late 1950s: without all the achievements in the quality of audio recording, there would be no "golden age" of audio of the time.

It was the period when the pioneering achievements of the 1930s spread throughout the whole world, and millions of people got the opportunity to enjoy the truly high fidelity of sound.

From 1954 to 1964, as television shifted from black and white to color, sound reproduction began to move from tabletop radio stations and massive "provincial French consoles" to elegant *stereo components*.

Gradually, the so-called *"separates"* — separate amplifiers, preamplifiers, record players with tape recorders and speakers — replaced console devices. It was then that the new official designation for the premium audio equipment being released at the time appeared — *hi-fi (high fidelity)*. Its implication was to bring the potential user's attention to a higher level of sound quality, made possible by, among other things, the functional separation of highly specialized components, selecting which — given enough skill (and luck) — a very decent system could be assembled on one's own.

Harry Pearson, retrospectively assessing the origins of high fidelity and of High End Audio that sprung out of it, remembered in our interview for *Audiomagazin* how in the 1950s and 1960s the market was mostly dominated by fairly primitive console-type systems (of the "all-in-one" kind) or DIY kits which could be bought at any large supermarket next to food sections, out of these kits enthusiasts would assemble audio equipment for their personal use.

At the same time audio consoles — radiolas and magnitolas — could, as a rule, only be bought at furniture stores (which is highly telling in terms of their positioning in the market).

In the early 60s brands that gave an impetus to a new segment of separate audio *components* — those same *separates* — began to win over in the US: *Bosac, Macintosh, Dynaco, Fisher.* Although high quality equipment was not only made in the US at the time, as the British-born editor of the American magazine *Stereophile* John Atkinson remembers, "... it was the US that emanated the energy that fueled the enthusiasm of equipment manufacturers throughout the rest of the world."

The audio industry's shift to separate components became a crucial milestone on the way to increasingly high-quality sound.

High End Audio as a class of especially high performance audio equipment will later be based on that same principal of *separate* components but on a different level: components of the hi-fi class, while separate, were positioned within purely utilitarian context of shallow entertainment and as such not advanced enough to allow the assembly of a system that would satisfy the most sophisticated and demanding listener.

During that interview at his house in Sea Cliff outside of New York in 2007 Pearson remembered: "Both then and now you would be unable to find a single audio manufacturer that would be capable of making every single system component as well as its competitors. Therefore, the liberalization of consumer choice allowed for the opportunity of achieving the best sonic results possible by combining the best components from different manufacturers."

But not for nothing — as they say, there are two sides to every coin. The transition from consoles to separates, along with all of its significant sonic improvement, also contained some serious contradictions. This substitution of the whole with separate parts became in some ways a kind of "shot in one's own foot". As instead of a finished product with audio components completely matched to each other, the user would purchase a fragmented set of "pre-fabricates", from which he had yet to assemble the finished system — which required making informed and reasonable choices. However, for many consumers who lacked both technical expertise and appropriate listening skills based on fully developed corresponding sonic ideological foundations and outlook those choices were as a rule far from being entirely conscious, and, as a rule, even not based on common sense.

Most importantly, with the component approach responsibility for the end result was transferred from equipment manufacturers and their dealers to consumers, who initially relished this newfound freedom. As is the case with every other kind of freedom, in terms of how productively they were able to use it, it happened to be a double-edge sword.

Such responsibility for the sonic end result born by the users themselves is further exacerbated by market globalization, because many potential customers from faraway places — as a result of their own various insecurities — partially due to all the cultural barriers which hinder the fluent perception of foreign cultural idioms, trust blindly the authoritative opinions of reviewers from the "audio metropolis", usually of American or European origin.

Dan D'Agostino, founder of *Krell Industries*, commenting on this predicament, once told me in an interview: "All in all, in terms of sound quality, there is no reference system even within the confines of a single music genre. I travel a lot and have noticed a long time ago how much sonic value systems and sound preferences differ from country to country. One of the reasons could potentially be that the difference in pronunciation in different languages, to some extent, form the notions of optimal audio system sound. For instance, Chinese and the Japanese ideas of high-quality sound do not correspond to these the Americans and the Brits share. Especially for classical music, given a large number of instruments and complexity of musical intonations. Moreover, if you own a system that adequately reproduces classical music, chances are that other genres of music will also sound good on it. However, I've heard thousands of systems that reproduce jazz music very well, yet many of them completely fail with classical recordings. With jazz, given a relatively decent system, one can achieve a magnificent musicians' presence effect and a feeling of a natural acoustic space. But, very often, as soon as you start playing classical music on the same system, it becomes evident at once that it is entirely worthless for this particular application."

One way or another, it is precisely within this field of immense opportunities and grave contradictions of the global audio industry of the late 1960s — early 1970s that High End Audio was born.

The arrival and initial development of High End Audio movement was driven by the desire of its participants — on both sides of the "sales counter barricades" — to revive its inherent mission of allowing unhindered access to "High Art" of the most subtle music appreciation via audio equipment and to imbue the hardware with all the necessary properties, while simultaneously countering the compromised approach of mass marketers to audio systems, as no more than a kind of home appliances, with an uncompromising ideal of absolute sound quality, the foundations of which we will discuss at length in the following chapter. As for this brief historical overview, we will conclude it at the dawn of a new, high-end, age of audio.

From Technology to Art

"In that era," a prominent English audio journalist **Ken Kessler** recalls in my interview with him for *Audiomagazin* in May 2007 "a range of various cultural, economic and technical factors came together, which defined an unprecedented rise of the whole audio industry. The hardware left furniture stores, and specialized audio salons began to appear, the great academic music performers of the 20th century were still alive, and charts included names that have not lost their significance even half a century later. All this became sufficient justification for investing in audio equipment of the highest caliber."

In the High End Audio segment such brands as *Audio Research Corporation, Magnepan, Dahlquist, Infinity, Mark Levinson, Vandersteen Audio, Conrad-Johnson, Krell Industries* and others came to the foreground during that time.

When the magazine *Stereophile* appeared at the end of the 60s everyone was taken aback by the critical ardor of its founder J. Gordon Holt. He saw his primary mission as guarding the interests of his readers (not his advertisers — yes, it was still possible back in the day!). Therefore, as in the magazine's very first issue he picked apart the — highly respectable at the time — full range electrostatic ACKLH-1 speakers, highlighting all of their virtues and, most importantly, all of their flaws, everyone from readers to the manufacturers themselves, so sure that they "owned" the specialized media, were in shock. Thus earning the respect of his magazine's readers, Holt gradually began to acquire the influence that not only allowed him to turn *Stereophile* into a highly successful publication but also gave him a large role to play in shaping the mindset of audiophiles all over the world.

Finally, the term "High End Audio" itself was introduced to the general public by the founder of *The Absolute Sound* magazine,

Harry Pearson, in 1973. This moniker not only underlined a new approach to both defining "absolute" sound quality itself and the methods to evaluate audio equipment made to reproduce it, but also the use of the special language developed by Pearson for the comprehensive description of the hardware's unique sonic properties.

The fact that it was the press that formed the ideological foundation for the industry and the information field around it is of paramount importance. As John Atkinson suggests, otherwise one would only be able to speak of a niche market rather than an actual industry.

The age-old question, "What came first, the chicken or the egg?" (i.e. what appeared first: a specialized press, creating some sort of a new ideology, based on which manufacturers then design consonant (sic!) equipment, or the other way round — equipment manufacturers, supporting a consonant (sic!) press which relays the ideology inherent in their designs to potential customers?) — was cleared up by Pearson himself in our interview:

"Spurring events on with our magazine publications, we influenced not just the readers, but also the manufacturers. Within their community a new generation appeared which would later form an entire industry. At the moment when our magazine started to be published, *Audio Research Corporation`s* founder **Bill Johnson** was working in a records store by day and tinkering with his amplifiers in his garage by night. But who would have found out about these amplifiers had it not been for our magazine?! Who would ever know that a new *revolutionary* offering has appeared on the market?!"

The need for Pearson's "subjective" language for describing audio equipment properties is a direct result of the audio industry's historical trajectory, along which no commonly accepted objective standard for assessing sound quality has ever been adopted. If at the dawn of audio this was due to a lack of necessary knowledge and equipment, lately, even with all of the scientific and technical conditions necessary for adopting adequate sound quality standards resistance came from the vast majority of established players in the industry: as the products of many of them may simply fall short of such a benchmark...

This duality of the "objective" and the "subjective" at the foundation of the High End Audio approach to assessing sound quality allows various players to stage a flurry of esoteric and pseudointellectual games around its specific sonic manifestations.

By the way, the younger video industry began in scientific and technological conditions of the post-WWII period, which, due to the appeared availability of appropriate measuring equipment and the required theoretical knowledge, allowed to form all-encompassing and commonly adopted image quality standards at its very onset. Such a firm grounding in the realm of precise objective knowledge served as the main reason for the consistent and rapid development of video technologies, as well as facilitating the elaboration of a precise paradigm for assessing image quality — as fully in line with a standard, nothing more.

As for the realm of audio, the necessity to keep the whole chain — from the manufacturer, through journalists, distributors, dealers, installers and others all the way to the customer — in mind when determining the appropriateness of one's own subjective position within it, is, conversely, the result of a lack of fundamental industry sound quality standards.

One of the most fundamental concepts in video technologies is "matching the resolution," that is to ensure the best image quality all along the recording and playback chain the equipment should operate in the same standard resolution mode. As audio resolution is still left not strictly defined, audiophiles have to stick to an alternative concept of "matching the virtue," that is, to ensure the best sound quality all along the recording and playback chain, they've got no other way than to rely on high moral and professional standards of all the human participants of that chain instead. In that sense, very stringent technical image quality standards in video are substituted — of course, to a certain degree only — with nothing more than just some general moral and professional standards in audio.

"The responsibility for the end result," Pearson emphasized, "needs to be shared between the manufacturers of separate components, the consumers themselves and, naturally, publications such as ours. That is, in fact, what we exist for — so that the customer is not left alone with a pile of incompatible building blocks, so that he can make a conscious and viable choice with our help."

In reality the selection process of chossing audio equipment boils doen to a very simple algorithm.. And despite the fact that crucial elements of the chain from manufacturer to the end user entirely omitted by Pearson — the distributors, dealers and installers — have as much of an effect on the end result with their actions and experience as the other links mentioned by him, all of the ultimate decisions made by the customer have to be guided by a very simple principle: *in established, after a certain period of maturation, chains such as these, sonic properties of both separate components and even assembled audio systems will be fully correlated with the subjective qualities of all the human links in them.* Actually, the secret of the art of High End Audio lies in the constant use of this basic subjective intuition.

Today, due to the fact that the peak of technical development and implementation of many technologies still actively used occurred in the 1920s — 1950s, there is constant talk of the end of High End Audio's history.

Despite the development of new digital formats their wide proliferation and the constantly changing menu of user functions of every kind, the overall quality of stereo sound has not been progressing for decades.

The only revolutionary impulse for audio that we can envision today is a widespread and consistent adoption of full-fledged 3D formats of sound recording and playback (for instance, in the context of re-creating a "virtual reality"). The first developments in the field confirm: the global shift from old-fashioned stereo to these new multichannel technologies will be as significant as the transition from black and white to color in television.

But for now, such a turn of events remains a thing of an uncertain future.

Chapter 3. The Dawn of High End Audio

From cradle to citadel

When one speaks of the origins of High End Audio and it`s special status that defines its separation from mere hi-fi (which often creates confusion, especially for an outside observer not infected with the virus of audiophilia) we inevitably end up discussing a juxtaposition between what can be termed *"audio primordialism"* and something that can (equally conditionally) be defined as *"audio constructivism."*

The so-called "audio primordialists" operate on the assumption that audio technology is rooted in an objective and evolutionary development process (akin to one that an evolving organism goes through, with a set of corresponding organs and functions), with the human factor — and all of its inherent meanings — removed. For them the difference between what has historically become hi-fi and High End Audio does not exist.

Relying on an objectivist worldview based on precise technical measurements, they are sure that High End Audio is the same old hi-fi. The very name "High-End" is, in this case, the result of a confusing *entity duplication.* Some "primordialists" take no issue with this duplication. Others aim to mercilessly rip to shreds the figment, in their opinion borne out of imagination, the naive gullibility of consumers and — should one dig deeper — the greed of manufacturers and dealers, with Occam's razor.

Nevertheless, if one refrains from reducing such duplication to its negative elements only, what can the term "High End Audio" mean? And why was it necessary at all, given the existence of a respectable and established over several decades predecessor — "hi-fi"?

Here, we end up in the so called "audio constructionist" camp. According to their creed, High End Audio and hi-fi are entirely different phenomena. What then is the difference? And where is the line separating the two?

The "constructionist" replies: the line lies in the realm of *cognitive constructs.*

Meaning that, despite uncritically assimilated platitudes — so the "constructivists" tell us — our entire "objective" reality is not really that objective. We confuse our own projections — that form us for generations and then cover their tracks — with objective and unchanging phenomena. Both "High Fidelity" and "High End Audio" are constructs. The difference between them lies not only in the hardware and its technical specifications, but the invisible cloud of values and meanings within which they have formed and continue to exist. Unlike the static hi-fi construct, the dynamic High End Audio construct is a *process,* a sphere of human activity that uses audio as means to an end within a value system framework with a set of corresponding criteria. These are the system of relationships and language, which reflect the person himself. Like music, High End Audio is not reduced to technology only with no artistic remainder.

A direct juxtaposition of these two constructs illuminates a fundamental difference between them. If the "high-quality reproduction of sound" of hi-fi established the level that has already been reached by the equipment, the "higher limit" of High End Audio has always represented an upcoming journey, opening up before a new dedicated listener. Thus, hi-fi is a *retrospective* project, while High End Audio is a *futuristic* one.

As a result of this juxtaposition, another term — located somewhere between the skies of High End Audio and the ground of hi-fi and in no way adding clarity for an outsider — appeared as a byproduct, intended to define an intermediary and unstable equilibrium between these two poles: "*mid-fi.*"

The views of both camps, the "audio primordialists" and the "audio constructivists", each in its own way, were conducive to audio equipment's ascent to today's sound quality levels.

As we were able to show in the previous chapter, the relentless and consistent quest for sound quality was largely rooted in the objective development of technologies, and it is that struggle that we have to thank for all the current achievements in the field that our predecessors could never have imagined.

At the same time, the medial (from the word "media") nature of High End Audio, existing at the intersection of technology and art, its humanistic purpose and its full compatibility with "our heart's aim", with a development vector that is co-directional to human inner growth, take us to the place where it becomes difficult to separate physics from semantics, chemistry from politics, economics from aesthetics.

So the purpose of High End Audio equipment does not boil down to perfectionism. The quest for perfection is merely a method of achieving certain instrumental properties of the equipment, necessary to realize its capabilities within the context of its intended functionality.

Therefore, *StereoPravda* — as is often the case — lies not in the extremes of a superstitious attitude to the subject at hand but in a deliberate and astute orientation in the auditory space (meaning, in this case, a space of the most precise, deepest and fullest perception of music through its sound reproduction).

High End Audio teaches us that clarity of understanding is inseparable from flexibility and the ability to adjust, to shift. First and foremost — between common sense and ideas that are "crazy enough to be true" (as Niels Bohr would say). To shift between being informed and the ability to be charmed; between practicality and risk; between pedantry and the capacity to let go, between the urge to "push to the end" and the ability to "stop in time", all this while not losing sight of the what's most important — Music, for which Hi-End exists.

Thus High End Audio appeared as a phenomenon in the late 1960s — early 1970s at the intersection of the following domains of:

— long-standing audio technologies;
— a special praxis with corresponding goals, values and descriptive language;
— established relationships between all the participants of the production, promotion, distribution, sales and consumption chains, in which this special praxis could be implemented and evolve.

IN UTERO

It is in fact not that important how truthful is the idea, widespread among audiophiles, that the term "High End Audio" was introduced by the editor of *The Absolute Sound* magazine, Harry Pearson. This myth has many staunch opposers. Nevertheless, if one accepts the notion that the phrase was known and used before Pearson it demonstrates yet again how engrained the construct is in the process of audio development itself and how much it was "hanging in the air" at its certain stage.

One way or another, the birth of High End Audio as a proper industry is closely associated with Harry Pearson and J. Gordon Holt, the people who managed to give the new phenomenon a space to form and develop freely on the pages of the magazines which they created and which posessed unquestionable authority.

Even before the appearance of the *Stereophile* magazine large Japanese corporations — like *Pioneer, Kenwood* (*Trio* to the rest of the world) and *Sansui* — have had the time to make themselves comfortable in the American market. By that point, the Japanese had significant experience in the manufacturing of transistor ("solid state" in audiophile lingo) audio equipment and were concentrating on consumer goods — while electronics manufacturing in the US was mostly limited to the military and industrial sectors. The Japanese manufactured products were sufficiently reliable and looked respectable enough; most importantly, they secured the support of popular consumer audio publications. Armed with the tricks and methods of mass promotion, the Japanese were better at selling their equipment in that stronghold of the free market than the Americans themselves.

Well-financed and business savvy — unlike the lagging American audio manufacturers — they were prepared to cover significant marketing expenses not only in specialized magazines but also in glossies like *Playboy*. Besides, they paid out daily generous bonuses from a special incentive fund ("SPIF") to thousands of their dealers. In the early 70s daily SPIF payments between 50 and 100 dollars were nothing unusual. For many vendors of Japanese electronics this became an offer they could not refuse.

When the American hi-fi industry in the beginning of the second half of the 20th century began to gradually decay because of these conditions, a pivotal role in giving it a new (or rather reviving the original) vigor and a new meaning was played by Holt, who got down to business with his usual sense of independence, dignity and sharp sense of humor.

In the late 60s *Stereophile* was a very different magazine from what it became thirty years later. It was a time when a tiny black and white "fanzine" would not publish "sell-out" ads on principle and was probably the only site where serious discussions were held not only on the sonic merits of various audio components but also about their flaws of all kinds — with a reader seeing a consistent strategy of attaining extraordinary sonic results form in front of him or her. *Stereophile*'s responsibility was, above all, to the readers, not the advertisers, and it performed a range of crucial functions: not only informing and fully educating the readers in good faith but also creating an appropriate market for them. Moreover, for the advertisers it played the role of a critic which did not allow successful manufacturers to rest on their laurels, thus stimulating their new designs and healthy competition.

GARAGE BIRTH

Meanwhile, here and there, in their garages across the whole world sound enthusiasts created new, well-forgotten old and sometimes exceptionally weird audio equipment. Garages (or even kitchen tables) served as laboratories. Galvanized by the ideas of the early *Stereophile*, they relished the opportunity to get their offering to an audience, and the nascent "by aficionados for aficionados" market gradually began to grow consistently: the number of companies in the US grew constantly. Several years later the new industry — rising from the ashes of an old one (hi-fi) — got its historical name: "High End Audio".

From the early 70s *Stereophile* was forced to share its primacy in the industry with *The Absolute Sound* magazine founded by Harry Pearson.

"Had the industry appeared without the influence of *Stereophile* and *The Absolute Sound*, which set the vector of its development," — the current editor of *Stereophile*, John Atkinson, shared during our interview — "the direction of High End Audio would not be as interesting and distinctive. It was Holt and Pearson who, back in the early 70s, inspired the idea in manufacturers that would later develop into a whole industry. One could accuse me — being a journalist myself — of exaggerating the role of magazines but that is not the case. It was the press that created the ideological foundations for the High End Audio industry and the information field around it."

Speaking of the influence that his magazine had on the market, Pearson told me:

"Our magazine covered only the most outstanding audio equipment, leaving ordinary and especially mediocre products out as if they had not existed for us at all. I personally knew many of the engineers and owners of companies that manufactured equipment and read everything that audio media published at the time. This gave me the certainty that I 'had my finger on the pulse', and that my magazine remained fully relevant, infallibly following its initial concept."

As for the term itself, Pearson shared some amusing details when I came to visit him in Sea Cliff.

"It was then that we found a definition for our interests — High End Audio. Although that term was used before us and not in the most decent of ways. Products existed, although in a very different area of interest that were sold in... sex shops — I am talking about *'high end' dildo*. If one was to get serious, we still had the task of defining the very notion of 'High End' ahead of us, having adopted it for our purposes as the most capacious, laconic and hardly leaving any hope for finding a suitable alternative."

Speaking of *Stereophile* and *The Absolute Sound* it is important to note that striving for the same goal, ploughing the same field, the publications were vastly different in style and material delivery. In many ways it was at this early stage that they already reflected the tension that would become a common thread weaving throughout the entire history — up until the present day — of High End Audio.

Namely, it is the dichotomy of the highest sound quality evaluation — between *objective knowledge descriptions* and *subjective perception declarations*.

Unlike his competitor, Holt largely relied on the objectivist model of audio[1]. Thus, in order to support the overall idea of the imperfections of a purely scientific and technical nature, *Stereophile*

---

[1] After leaving the magazine in the 90s and until the end of his days (he died in 2009), Holt continued to take active part in the work of the *Audio Engineering Society*.

continued to emphasize it in its editorial policy, reflected in an active use of technical measurements for equipment reviews. At the same time, *The Absolute Sound* purposefully avoided the scientific jungle, believing that an accurate perception of high-quality sound relies on the aesthetic, rather than technical, development of the listener. Promoting the notions necessary for this development formed the primary mission of Pearson's magazine.

Against the backdrop of "objectivist", purely commercial, consumer audio magazines of the time (such as the American *Stereo Review* and *Audio*), *Stereophile* and *The Absolute Sound* were undoubtedly of the same creed as they were both rocking the boat of opportunistic conformity. Nevertheless, the very polemic that they were engaged in showed in the differing discourses they chose in the context of a lack of commonly accepted standardization of audio equipment, reflected real difficulties in assessing component quality and the precision of its criteria.

Stereophile readers criticized Pearson for his complete rejection of all technical measurement procedures. The fans of *The Absolute Sound* reasonably pointed out the deficiencies of the measurements (usually "static") provided in Holt's magazine, which were only remotely correlated with the real sound of the equipment and provided no explanation as to why two loudspeakers with almost identical — according to the measurements — characteristics could have a tenfold difference in price, for example!

As a consequence of these fundamental differences in choosing the points of focus and the juxtaposition of the "subjective" and the "objective", these publications always offered slightly different explanations for various methods and phenomena — such as, for instance, the main drawbacks of "blind" equipment auditioning tests. They also differed in what they required from their authors, as well as the other numerous *pro et contra* typical of High End Audio.

THE FIRST WORDS

The gradual formation by the combined efforts of the two magazines of what can already be called the established *language of High End Audio* is a separate and important topic.

As the bearer of the "gold standard" in audio journalism, Pearson, thanks to his deep love of music and a clear vision of High End's primary mission, was able to infect hundreds of thousands of audiophiles across the world with his enthusiasm. The vocabulary that he developed became the dialect that audiophiles still use to communicate with each other and which allowed for a full-fledged audiophile equipment criticism to emerge.

Pearson told me in conversation:

"I had to develop the publication concept myself, invent a new system of values and signposts, as well as a new terminology that would be capable of reflecting and juxtaposing these values, moreover — one that would be intelligible not only to myself, but to all the readers as well.

For *The Absolute Sound* the process of developing the terminology and vocabulary was, I would say, the most critical stage of its formation. However, in my opinion, we passed it successfully. We have our own, original, style of expression, allowing the reader to easily grasp technical concepts (given that we've never done measurements), expand his perspective and make conscious choices, based on his or her priorities and preferences — all with the help of our published materials.

For instance, as I was starting out I came up with — and began to use frequently — the term 'stage width'. This merely meant the width of the totality of stereo images on the recording meaning that it is an ordering of stereo images from right to left. No one used this expression before me. I was made fun of at first: 'Stage width… — what does that even mean?' What I actually meant was one of the dimensions of the three-dimensional sonic space. Many of these expressions that I invented were a consequence of wanting to describe what I was hearing, without trying to fantasize. However, what I was hearing was already based on my existing auditory experience. You have to understand that many people do not even attempt to listen closely. But they will be able and willing to do so if you give them the necessary tools. And these tools are the use of a specific language and expressions."

When reading audio equipment reviews today in all sorts of magazines and on audio Internet forums, audiophiles take for granted such expressions as *"soundstage depth and layering"*, *"image focusing"*, *"microdynamics"*, *"dynamic contrasts"*, *"palpability"* and *"air"*. Most of them were introduced by Harry Pearson.

At the same time, the *creed* of the manufacturers and the growing industry was — and couldn't not be — based on a harmony with the listener's fundamental investigative quests and reader needs. This gave a clear direction to High End Audio's intensive development.

The symbol of true audiophiles' faith was perhaps most clearly reflected in two aspects. First, in the definition given by Harry Pearson to *"absolute sound"*. Second — in the two formulas that will eventually be awarded the status of the *two Fundamental Laws of High End Audio*.

By way of illustrating what, thanks to Pearson, was defined within High End Audio as the ultimate goal (for both the listener and the other players), one can think of a photograph, fairly well-known among older generation of audiophiles. It shows a demonstration — somewhere among trees and shrubbery — organized by Edgar Villchur (*Acoustic Research*) of his "AR-3" loudspeakers. During the demonstration, the reproduced recording is compared to none other than the same piece played by... a string quartet. This became the visible manifestation and a graphic illustration of that very concept of "absolute sound", which Harry Pearson called the goal and primary criterion of assessing system quality: *"The most accurate and holographic audio reproduction of the sound of acoustic instruments played in a natural acoustic space."*

> Interestingly, decades later, in 2009, our company, *StereoPravda*, held a presentation of the Danish manufacturer *Steinway-Lyngdorf*'s "Model D" stereo system at the Moscow House of Music, where that same idea was brought to life by comparing a live performance of four musicians playing two *Steinway* concert "Model D" grand pianos with the sound of *Steinway-Lyngdorf*'s — "Model D" as well! — stereo system. The SL loudspeaker and the "head unit" — sandwiched between the five (!) grand pianos and at some moments up to eight musicians on stage — were reproducing a recording of Ravel's "Bolero", specifically made for the occasion and performed by four of those very same musicians on the same instruments and in the same concert hall — with the goal of having the audience "feel the difference" (pre-scheduled breaks in the live performance that musicians took were filled with the playback of corresponding score fragments that they themselves pre-recorded in the same spot through the audio system).

According to the concept of "absolute sound", that sets up a system of coordinates, the two Fundamental Laws of High End Audio were intended to describe the logic within which the desired effect becomes attainable in principle. Given the fact that we are considering the overall sonic result, in spite of detailed reviews of separate components, by the original intent of its forefathers, the foundation of High End included a fully *systemic approach* to assessing the overall sound quality for a given set of equipment.

However, any of the High End manufacturing firms has its own twist on the fundamental concepts of sound quality and its own — distinctive — technical means of implementing them. What then does this difference in private positions entail and which of the various parts of them can be emphasized?

By way of an illustration, I will use several quotes from interviews I conducted throughout the years for *Audiomagazin*.

Richard Murry, head of *True Sound Works*: "The goal appeared of its own accord: to reach such a high quality of music reproduction that a recording of an orchestra will sound like a *real live* orchestra. The sound of the best loudspeakers should get as close as possible to *natural* sound. When one listens to such systems, it seems that they are 'creating' music out of *the air* itself. Compared to speakers that I hold up as perfect, I would describe the others as more *colored*."

Dan D'Agostino, founder of *Krell Industries*: "Our main goals always remained the same, the things that have changed are the means of achieving them. Specifically, our main goal is to transmit *all of the information* contained on the sound storage medium *with zero losses*."

Carl Marchisotto, head of *Nola Speakers*: "Our company's acoustic systems have to reproduce sound as *accurately* as possible. The more alike it is to 'live' sound, the better. At the heart of our company's approach lies a *lack of any sound colorations*. We want to create audio systems with the most *transparent* and *clear* sound. There are probably fans of another kind of sound — pleasant, yet inaccurate — but we are not among them. We are in favor of an *airy* and *open* sound, and our systems are recognized for these qualities across the globe."

Steve Nugent, head of *Empirical Audio*: "I do not strive to make my gear sound simply beautiful and soft. That type of sound is not alive at all. And that goal is fairly easy to achieve with a mediocre tube amplifier, or by rolling off high frequencies, or by applying sound compression. My goal is to extract *all 100 per cent of the dynamic range and high frequency information* contained on the recording. And to keep the *noise and distortion levels to a minimum.* When this goal is achieved, everything that was previously hidden or concealed in a recording comes out into the open. Including not only the sound's physical body, but the music's emotional content. This is what this whole *audiophilia* — which, on the opposite, is engaged in endless listening to music fragments with the goal of assessing the physical aspects of the process — should revolve around. And what I am talking about is that moment of bliss when the listener begins to involuntarily tap his foot to the beat, or tears unwittingly come to his or her eyes."

Were one to summarize the above, the point of the existence of High End Audio equipment lies in the opportunity to create *honest* systems and convey musical *truth* to those who are truly seeking it.

GROWING PAINS: FROM THE WHOLE TO ITS PARTS

The 1980s were the time when the audio industry became acutely aware of the fact that each one of the separate components in the audio signal chain has to be meticulously evaluated in terms of its effect on sound degradation. However, as subsequent experience taught us, the blinded insistence on the separate componerts' ultimate sound quality lead to complete forgetfulness regarding another type of degradation to run rampant... the degradation of the most fundamental principles of assembling the complete audio systems.

This unfortunate state of oblivion had the most profound and controversial consequences for the entire High End Audio industry.

On one hand it should have been apparent from the start that for attaining results of the highest quality a systemic approach has to be employed at all levels of implementation, from choosing the dealer for purchasing and installing the audio system to the choice of each of its separate components. All of High-End's extraordinary achievements have always been and still are related to maintaining that systemic approach — just like all of the dead ends and traps into which many of its short-sighted adherents fell have always been and are to this day caused by ignoring it.

On the other hand, an increasing reliance on manufacturers who became the main advertisers[2] and who generally made — as a result of their garage origins and therefore small production capacity — separate components rather than fully assembled audio

---

[2] In our interview, Harry Pearson shared how every attempt to create an audio magazine with no ads crashed and burned due to the reader's unwillingness to pay for it; the appearance of *Xerox* copy machines, when greedy and short-sighted readers copied each other's magazines, put an end to such attempts entirely, turning magazines into the hostages of their advertisers — which, in turn, made them increasingly dependent on manufacturers.

systems, forced the specialized media to succumb to the "separate components" approach, focusing the audience's attention on the difference in sound quality not of complete systems but separate components.

That would be like if car magazines would had provided all the detailed descriptions of various carburetors, transmissions and steering wheels from different manufacturers, and at the same time would had completely ignored the properties of fully assembled cars (and would had not given a damn about where and how they are assembled — or even would had suggested to do it yourself!). As a rule, the content of today's audio magazines resembles, to continue with this analogy, a set of colorful ads for various automobile's spare parts, implying a choice of "the most ideal" ones and then suggesting a car's manual assembly on one's own — with a complete lack of ads for either finished cars or dealers, from whom these fully assembled cars can be purchased.

Sounds absurd?! Unfortunately, it doesn't to High End Audio's key players. The vast majority of them stubbornly believe that inciting the audiophile crowd to mindless creativity will allow them to earn a bigger buck than purposefully promoting a truly systemic approach to audio system assembly and installation at all levels. At the very least, that has always been their short-term plan.

Having chosen the "component" approach as the principal method of the promotion and selling of audio systems, thus pointing every audiophile towards a search for some set of abstract "ideal" components, the industry has gradually, through a system of checks and balances, formulated what can be called the *two Fundamental Laws of High End Audio*.

These laws have been floating in the ether of the audiophile discourse as nothing more than intuitive feelings, until suddenly — the exact date is hard to determine — being condensed into concrete statements.

It goes without saying how much these laws contradicted the established wisdom of the consumer society, with consumers wanting ever more — and for less and less money ("the customers are always right", aren't they?!)...

As Lenin put it in one of his works, "one cannot live in a society and be free from it." Unfortunately, for many participants of High End Audio games (on both sides of the "sales counter barricades") due to the prevalent stereotypes of contemporary society these laws, initially intended to stimulate the productive development of High End Audio, were ultimately turned inside out. But first things first.

Rebel Rebel

A. "The Law of Diminishing Returns"

The first of the two laws of High End Audio is the *Law of Diminishing Returns*. This law postulates the necessity of coming to terms with decreasing returns in terms of sound quality with the ever increasing amount of resources expended — effort, time and money, motivating audiophiles to go further and further down their chosen path in audio. Sounds like a paradox for a consumer society and a rebellion against its very nature, doesn't it?

While every truly productive approach has global ideas behind it, as a rule, the problem lies in the fact that, generally, truly important ideas are left out of focus, glossed over by the palliative approach popular with the commercial mainstream, in which secondary factors push the primary ones aside.

But only fundamental global principles can ensure a serious, full-fledged breakthrough in sound quality, whereas the mainstream continues to nudge listeners to inconsequential decisions that can deliver a result which, while registered by the human ear, is ultimately flawed and — in the context of overall sound quality — altogether fragmentary.

Thus, only a purposeful and deliberate planning allows to attain the optimal effect, and only a systemic approach provides the opportunity to adequately assess each of the every given sonic return at the audio component level, while simply looking at isolated improvements on a "component" level only, outside the context of a given audio system, usually leads to unreasonable expenses, unjustified in the context of the overall sonic return.

Rather than fussing about all sorts of "audio trivia", it is far more productive to look for *macroscopic* means of improvement. Such means are usually determined by a proper evaluation of priorities and are found off the mainstream beaten track with its marketing based on the paradigm of widest possible (pseudo) choice between almost indistinguishable audio components. As with everything else of significance, these paths of the meaningful improvement are far away from the tired secondary and tertiary, in terms of their sonic importance, solutions that focus the attention of a much-too-gullible public on dubious accessories of every kind — *snake-oil* tweaks, exotic isolation cones or, for instance, equipment stands at the price of a decent car.

Speaking of a system of priorities based simply on common sense, the most important macroscopic paths of assembling an audio system of the highest caliber are related to the choice of (in order of decreasing significance):

(1) the means for the optimal acoustic treatment of the listening room;

(2) optimal speaker positioning in that room;

(3) if possible, an "active" multi-way configuration of the appropriate loudspeakers and corresponding tools for their "voicing" (as opposed to "passive" one-way configuration);

(4) an appropriate set of loudspeakers and then amplifiers to drive them properly;

(5) appropriate cutting-edge source components of the highest resolution;

and so forth.

The absence of specialized cables on this list does not mean that all of them sound the same. However, they should obviously not be the top priority while making the most important decisions regarding the audio systems' configuration (this can cause a cognitive dissonance for an outside observer, given the sheer scale of this product category's presence on the market).

Most "macro"-effect solutions come either from the distant past — not yet muddled by the existence of large numbers of gullible "dummies" or from the not too distant future, which those "dummies" are barred from entering — therefore, these solutions remain purposefully unnoticed by the commercial mainstream, aimed at short-term gains here and now.

For instance, the fundamental idea that, in order to get a sound of an extraordinarily high quality, the equipment has to, at the very least, look *extraordinary*, lies on the surface.

Considering the fact that the listening room is a key component of the system, it too should, in theory, look unusual as a result of maximum preparation for the goal of attaining the absolute sound.

Correspondingly, nothing costs so little and is valued so much as a correct physical positioning of an acoustic system in a correctly prepared acoustic space.

Precisely for this reason the vast majority of even the most expensive audio systems will generally sound entirely unimpressive in "raw" — acoustically speaking — environments.

The most simple analogy here is as follows.

> Imagine — you arrive at a movie theatre, buy the popcorn, get comfortable in your seat, put your arm around your girlfriend, the film is starting, you are eagerly anticipating it… but — darn it! The projectionist forgot to turn off the light! And the film keeps on going. Comments are coming from all over the theatre: "If only they would connect the projector with a different video cable and put it on top of such and such isolation cones — that would make all the difference!" While the light remains on…

The point is that fundamental ideas cannot be realized with a mere set of superficial gimmicks. Turning off the light in a movie theater is an essential part of preparing the specialized environment for watching a film. There are no other ways of doing it, and the result one gets from it, compared to the effort involved, is enormous.

The same conclusion applies to the effect of listening room acoustic properties on the audio system's sound quality.

In order to not only understand this point but also act in accordance with it a fairly high degree of expertise, skill and experience are required, without which "passing the buck" to beginner users, in terms of the fundamental decisions that they have to make, is nothing short of a malicious exploitation of neophytes. It results in endless walking in circles along a flat curve of sonic returns against unreasonable expenses, with no real growth, leading merely to ephemeral increases in insignificant micro results.

The chance to remain on the linear growth part of the curve of improving sound quality against the resources and efforts expended is only insured by using fundamental and significant ideas.

Avoiding a head-on collision with the *law of diminishing returns* is only made possible by employing new (or, rather, well-forgotten old) principles which support consistent growth due to their potential for macro changes in sound, not through the proverbial "arms race", in which the consumer thoughtlessly commits ever increasing resources to insignificant or outdated ideas and technologies.

All of the heated debates over which amplifier or which speaker is better as well as audio equipment reviews that are detached from the most fundamental ideas force the audiophiles onto the part of the *law of diminishing returns* curve where these returns are increasingly diminishing, where the difference in sound quality becomes entirely immaterial and such debates empty. And no matter how much of a paradox, this is especially evident from an outside perspective, when these ever less and less diminishing returns are perceived by the ears of ordinary music lovers — ears that have not been spoiled by all of these audiophile squabbles and entirely uninterested in them[3].

Many audiophiles fall for diminishing returns in sound quality only as a result of their immaturity. While actually they are entitled to much more significant returns for the efforts and resources usually committed than they realize.

B. "Omission But Not Commission"

The second Fundamental Law of High End Audio is that of *Omission But Not Commission*, roughly meaning "less is more". Again, in the context of the absolute consumerism of recent years this sounds like blasphemy.

Unlike the hi-fi equipment that preceded High End Audio — where the fundamental goal was to achieve a certain *fullness* and *richness* of tone (usually with an added sonic "bonus"[4] on top of the proposition), High End Audio, on the other hand, always insisted on maximizing *"musical resolution"* — both in terms of frequency and time domains. Only with the desired sound presentation (see the previous chapters) achieved can the remaining resources —

---

[3] All of our ears are created equal; therefore, the difference between a seasoned audiophile and a layman lies not in determining which demonstration sounds good and which doesn't (laymen are perfectly capable of doing this on their own), but in predictably and consistently making a demo to sound exceptional.

[4] In the form of achieving, for instance, excessive loudness levels or reproducing an exaggerated, infra-bass from the "depths of Hell'.

given a certain budget — be used for various secondary pursuits: for instance, maximizing the reproduced frequency range (especially at its edges), as well as maximizing macrodynamics (i.e. maximizing the overall dynamic range for increasing available playback levels). Under macro sonic returns policy flashy luxury embellishments are supposed to be implemented with whatever funds remained.

While the uninitiated fans of hi-fi were prepared to sacrifice musical micro resolution on the altar of "full" and "meaty" sound character with a fully extended thundering bass and very high loudness levels, High End Audio adepts were ready to part with its "visceral impact", bass extension and available loudness levels in order to maintain the highest musical resolution along the whole micro-temporal dynamic development loop of the music signal including the ultimate resolution ("articulation") of the bass frequencies. To a great extent, this position was validated by the fact that the object of their passion — "serious" music — was always taken to mean *acoustic* music in which most of its semantic meaning is located in the middle of the frequency range, not at its edges. Accordingly, this Second Law assumed that a lack of infra-low bass or the highest frequency extension would not have a significant effect on the overall "digestibility" of these music genres and result in only a minor loss in overall macrodynamic impact.

From this another wording of the *Omission But Not Commission* principle arises: "Too little is better than too much." The "less is more" principle, as in medicine, has been declared in High End Audio from the very beginning, meaning that it is of paramount importance not to "hurt" the sound presentation.

Besides the stated movement towards the "absolute", albeit with tiny steps, High End Audio has historically arisen from the fundamental postulate that, given a finite budget, the musical *"micro resolution"* of an audio system is of primary importance, whereas sound "density", meaning achieving the highest saturation of sonic "*contrasts*" across the whole frequency range and along the whole dynamic loop of the audio signal's natural temporal development are secondary. Initially this Law facilitated a very positive trend of forming some new offshoots within acoustic and electronic research fields began to develop within High End Audio.

As the physical properties of the main materials (especially magnetic ones) have been fully exhausted by previous generations of audio engineers the search for appropriate new solutions led in the direction opposite to that of previous ones. Instead of horn loaded loudspeakers with the highest efficiency and high impedance mated to relatively low-powered amplifiers new loudspeakers with ever lower efficiency and lower (and also increasingly complex and thus most difficult for small-Watts amps) impedance were introduced to the market as well as increasingly powerful amplifiers capable of driving low impedance and low efficiency loads, unmanageable for lesser amplifiers.

Ribbon loudspeaker systems, for instance, appeared naturally during the search for the lightest loudspeaker sound radiating elements with virtually no inertia. For example, the aluminum foil in a *Magnepan* speaker's tweeter — rolled out to a thickness of a few microns — is lighter than the amount of air that it moves.

The emergence of such new technologies, both in loudspeaker design and accompanying electronics, proved the validity of a new, high-end, direction in audio, especially for the connoisseurs of serious acoustic music. It became clear that the new generation of this equipment allows to hear a much larger amount of musically significant information in a given unit of time than has been possible before.

But everything has its price. At the same time, as the laws of physics remained in place, as with video — where attaining a higher resolution on the screen while maintaining brightness, a full color gamut and dynamic range inevitably leads to a slew of technical issues and a drastic increase in the price of video systems — it became necessary for audio to develop and affirm some new system of values and compromises with the goal of affixing various levels of quality and price as well as different functions. This system was termed *Omission But Not Commission* by High End Audio's ideologues. And to prosper the industry does need to continue to implement this Law too.

As with modern video where one can change several key parameters except the primary one (the original maximum pass-through resolution of the signal chain itself) in audio one can change various parameters — timbre, possible loudness levels and dynamic range width — with the exception of one: the original maximum "musical resolution" of the audio signal chain as a whole.

In both video and audio the *transducer*, a device that transforms one form of energy into another, usually becomes the "bottleneck" in terms of this original resolution. In video that is the display, in audio — the loudspeakers. Not only storage medium resolution types but also the maximum resolution of the audio signal chain's other components should be adapted to match the maximal transducer resolution. To achieve maximum image quality the universally accepted concept exists in video — "signal pass-through resolution matching along the entire signal path". In theory, such a concept should also exist in audio.

The Omission But Not Commission law is based on the idea that the level of musical resolution of a system determines its *baseline level of quality*. Accordingly, *the higher this baseline resolution, the higher the quality of the audio system.* Ongoing support of this resolution while striving for ever increasing fullness and richness of reproduced sound requires additional but not absolutely essential funds, despite the fact that they — through their ability to ensure the completeness of sound — actually determine the *final baseline* quality level of the audio system.

These two Laws were instrumental in consolidating a range of conceptual, technical and economic positions among industry players. This ensured the rapid growth of the industry at its early development stages, and by the late 1980s it gradually began to enter a period of maturity that can be appropriately described as its Golden Age.

Chapter 4. THE GOLDEN AGE

A SLIGHTLY SENTIMENTAL JOURNEY

DIZZY WITH SUCCESS

"**J**esus, there are so many beautiful and smart people around!", an American representative of one of the logistical companies working with *Purple Legion*[1] once exclaimed at a reception, organized by the *Stereophile* magazine at the *CES-1996* trade show in Las Vegas. "Your industry is so fascinating!"

A crowd of young and energetic people was bustling around us, enthusiastically talking to each other for hours on end.

Yes, in those times, when audio was at the epicenter of the *Consumer Electronic Show*, High End Audio was, as they say, "blazing a trail".

In those times the smug appearances of Dan D'Agostino, president of *Krell Industries* in front of his dealers in enormous conference halls of Las Vegas hotels during CES were constantly

---

[1] At that point, one of the most advanced store chains that sold music CDs, vinyl records and DVDs in Russia. *PL* also had a division (which I was in charge of between 1992 and 2002) that distributed High End Audio products with quite extensive portfolio of the American-made gear. The hardware division operated a flagship retail store in Moscow.

interrupted with thunderous and long-lasting applause — just like years before, when the speeches of the General Secretaries of the Soviet Communist Party were interrupted at the Party Congresses.

Krell returned the loyalty in spades by throwing parties at the CES, like the one I was present at, in the enormous banquet hall at Caesars Palace in January 1998 — the year when a severe economic crisis broke out. Given the amount of food, drink and entertainment provided, it resembled a feast for a Roman emperor (including a crowd of half-naked body builders that would give a massage to anyone who was interested).

It was also during that time that I lived through my "fifteen minutes of fame" when a flight attendant on an *Aeroflot* flight from Los Angeles to Moscow asked me for an autograph, suddenly seeing me among the passengers as he was reading the latest issue of *Salon AV*, a Russian magazine with one of my articles in it, in a back seat during the flight.

All in all, the spirit of those times became fully resonant with High End Audio, filling with euphoria every participant of the industry that was at the very peak of demand and success.

In the context of the global history of technology those were the last "pre-Internet" days. No one was yet concerned with the upcoming digitalization of everything, the process completely indifferent to the semantic core of High End Audio and the ensuing oppression of its potential by the all-mighty Digit that were at the doorstep and will soon announce (jointly with some other "black swans" of the industry) the beginning of its decline. But this will happen a little later.

For now the untethered creativity of the masses within the highest audio segment continued to bloom...

BACK IN THE USSR

From the mid-1980s — as the winds of "perestroika" began to blow and the previously impenetrable Iron Curtain around socialist countries began to thin — a swarm of foreign journalists and Western media representatives headed towards the USSR, some of them simply naive, some with "shady" intentions. Among them were reporters from music publications like the *New Musical Express* and the *Rolling Stone*, political commentators from the *New York Times*, looking for a "scoop", sons of American cultural attaches doing freelance writing about the Soviet "counter-culture" phenomenon, as well as musicians of all kinds: the first openly advertised USSR tours by an American pop-rock superstar Billy Joel and some of the most popular independent British bands (*UB-40*) happened during this period. Numerous modern (anti-?) art celebrities did not fail to take advantage of the confusion that arose in the USSR and rushed there to establish their actual presence at the avalanche of the cultural tectonic shifts.

After graduating from the faculty of experimental and theoretical physics of the Moscow Engineering and Physics Institute (MEPhI) where I majored in solid state physics and following the irresistible urge to pursue my music aspirations I consciously burned all the bridges with the official establishment and stepped onto the treacherous — from the Soviet political bureaucrats' standpoint — path of "unofficial art" where all phenomena — including musical ones — were judged exclusively by their degree of nonconformity. None of us cultural outcasts could have imagined that by the end of the 1980s the winds of political change will suddenly begin blowing in our sails...

It was in this rapidly changing scenery of 1987 that I met the British DJ **John Peel** in Moscow, with whom we would later develop a close friendship. John Peel was at that point perhaps the ultimate authority in new music, he was forming musical tastes in Britain and discovering new names in music, for which he earned the unofficial title of a "National Institution." In the following years I would stay at his house in Suffolk — a two-hour drive from London — several times, and he even invited me for an interview in one of his BBC programs. As throughout the preceding years my musical tastes had been formed under his direct influence, a possible reason for us getting so close could be that in me he saw an embodiment of the meaning of his own work at BBC World Service as he was able to influence minds even behind the seemingly impenetrable Iron Curtain.

As a matter of fact, back in my student days in order to find out as much as possible about the music that interested me as well as the most up-to-date musical events I concentrated on learning English by myself, and in those days in the USSR it meant sitting for days on end glued to a speaker of a shortwave radio receiver — to hear native speech.

Because all radio programs in Russian were heavily jammed by the authorities programs in foreign languages were the only available channel for obtaining relevant information. The USSR had always leaned more towards British (and European) music than American one (why, it's a long story, but to make it short, the reasons are the more overlapped cultural background and the relative geographical proximity), so the BBC World Service programs became my primary source of new musical information. To compile a program schedule I had to spent a whole month listening to them 24 hours a day, 7 days a week with short breaks for sleeping — as there was simply no other way to get it done.

The Soviet authorities left foreign language broadcasts alone because the shortwave radio jam transmitters located on Soviet territory were capable of reaching far beyond its borders, which would naturally cause serious international scandals and, considering that hardly anyone among the general population spoke a foreign language or even knew one at a level of passive understanding such conflicts weren't really worth it within the overall scheme of struggle against the "corrupting influence of the West."

Such a peculiar manifestation of my passion for music was not an exclusively Soviet idiosyncrasy — driven by a general deficit — at the time. As pompous as it may sound today, the attitude towards music all over the world at the time was — in the very literal sense of the word — sacral. It was through music that my generation paved the way to the highest truths. Music was the *only true signal.* What's more, this expression is not rooted in the Soviet dissident's vocabulary at a time when "there was no news in *Pravda* and no truth in *Izvestia.*" [2] I have borrowed it from a book on the perception of popular music written several years ago by **Daniel Levitin**, former *Talking Heads* guitarist turned a respectable psychology researcher.

In full compliance with this status of the *"only true signal"* the High End Audio industry — as it appeared to me at the very beginning of the 90s — made the impression that its main purpose was the construction of veritable musical altars at which the obsessed music worshippers could search for the highest Truth and pray to their musical gods. And these aren't just words. I myself had a feeling of (audiophile) *"flow"*, as the inner state was designated lately.

> I understand now that audio systems that — in words of a great Russian proletarian writer Maxim Gorky — *"were born to crawl, they cannot fly"* and vice versa.

[2] *Pravda* and *Izvestia* were two of the most widely circulated Soviet newspapers. "Pravda" is Russian for "truth", "izvestya' is Russian for "news".

The internal vectors of the customers' emotional and intellectual growth dispositions-either "up" or "down" — make the choices for them. So that, either the adherence to depressive/conformist/opportunist general mental attitudes or a propensity for an inner state of a passionate *"flow"* (or, *"flight"*, in alternative lingo) drive them to correspondingly opposite purchasing decisions and products, which, further strengthening the momentum, pull their inner growth/personal development perspectives either further "up" or "down." Likewise, the audio manufacturers, driven by those same forces, either imbue or do not imbue their products with such *"high fly aerodynamics"* sonic qualities.

During my senior years at MEPhI I dived head-first into the crowd of "unofficial" Saint Petersburg and Moscow rock bands, organized concerts of *Akvarium, Sergey Kuryokhin, Mike Naumenko, Kino, Strannye Igry, Tsentr* and others at the "Rockwell Kent" club in the basement of my dormitory. My relationships with these musicians were not limited by just my promotional efforts for their live gigs. They were based on mutual attraction to each other due to my encyclopedic knowledge of music they were also very interested in, knowledge sourced from rare foreign magazines which I would buy in the black market for exorbitant price, as well as radio programs which I continued to listen to with an ever-increasing understanding of spoken English. These new acquaintances determined my fate for the next decade.

Being in a state of euphoria caused by listening to new music of all kinds and the feeling of the powerful resonance with the *Zeitgeist*, I hadn't even noticed how a new era was approaching. The dizziness caused by the changes prevented the realization of the scale of what was happening to me (and to all of my compatriots) at the time.

On my first foreign trip to London in 1990, when at the afterparty following a concert of a top music producer at the time, **Daniel Lanois**, at a small London restaurant, in a single room I could chat to Bob Dylan, Van Morrison, Edge from *U2*, Annie Lennox, Alison Moyet, famous photographer Anton Corbijn and then bump into Elvis Costello at the men's room. Back then I suddenly began to take all of this for granted. A brief backstage conversation with David Bowie during the intermission of his *Tin Machine* London concert at the Brixton Academy was like "Oh, I forgot to ask him about that Young Americans song's arrangements." A personal Factory tour by Andy Warhol's right-hand man, Bob Colacello, followed by dinner at Bridgette Berlin's (one of Andy's "girls") apartment — sure, why not?! And then a few days later to have dinner with Bob Weir (bass player for the *Grateful Dead*) at his manager Barbara Whitestone's San Rafael house and listening to their conversation while driving across the Golden Gate Bridge in her convertible for a Screamin' Jay Hawkins' concert (to say hello to him at his dressing room after the performance) was like a dream that suddenly came true.

> The reason I am recounting all of this is not only to show the context of my life on the brink of my discovery of High End Audio but also to contemplate one of the fundamental causes of the phenomenon's current crisis, which I would call a *demographic* one. By that I mean a tectonic shift in significance of music in our societies: from a generation that believed in it as a religion to the next one that saw it as no more than just one of a kind of easily accessible types of entertainment.

Today it is impossible to imagine that back in the 90s a large part of successful young people here in Russia first bought audio equipment — having dreamt about it all of their life — and only then would begin thinking about purchasing a car or an apartment. What's more, for the sake of the "purity of the experiment", I have to note that, in post-Soviet Russia the costs were very close (a guy I knew bought his first studio apartment in a not too remote town in Urals for a hundred kilograms of butter, which he somehow — despite persistent shortages at the time — managed to get his hands on!).

It is therefore not an exaggeration to say that the main problem of High End Audio today lies in the fact that it is still trying, running on fumes, to sell musical "church utensils" to the increasingly atheistic, serious music-wise, society. It is noteworthy that the customary free placement of a Bible in every American hotel room has also ceased during the same time — seemingly for very similar reasons.

By the age of thirty my constant spins in numerous orbits around the epicenter of music could only lead me to transition to yet another one. It happened in 1990 — a highly significant year for me.

A NEW ORBIT

Due to a multitude of favorable economic and political factors (including just opened new markets behind the Iron Curtain and a sudden unrestricted availability of vacuum tubes from "red" (socialist) countries for next to nothing) the High End Audio industry, that was growing gradually for some time, then out of the blue exploded at the beginning of the 1990s, and a previously unseen boom has began. The *Stereophile* magazine, the circulation of which was steadily growing from 3,000 copies in 1982 to almost 50, 000 in 1989, swelled immediately — both in its size and the number of copies that were distributed (reaching 92,000 at the peak of its circulation in 1994).

The era of numerous specialized *audio boutiques* and *audio shows* began to approach its zenith.

One April day in 1990 the shock wave from this "explosion" reached me, throwing my revolutions in the circles around my Saint Petersburg "unofficial" musician friends onto an entirely new musical orbit.

During my first visit to San Francisco I had saved five hundred dollars for a new audio gear (let me clarify: at the time, it was forbidden to take over fifty dollars out of the USSR, the average monthly salary around the country being about as much). Feverishly imagining what I would be able to buy with that money (a good quality cassette deck first and, possibly, an amplifier for my *Bose*-901 loudspeakers, second), I sheepishly wandered around large audio equipment stores, mostly window shopping.

One day leafing through local newspapers, looking for sales ads in the living room of my friend Alan Robinson at whose place I was staying, I saw an inconspicuous magazine, a brochure with a magical name *Stereophile* lying in a pile of publications on the coffee table.

When I have opened it, I was stunned: sky-high prices, unknown company names and — compared to the "hip" design of contemporary Japanese stuff — a very old-fashioned look of the most expensive equipment.

Replying to my question "What is that?" Alan immediately informed me that he was invited for a reception at a local audio salon that evening (*Stereo+* on Market Street), and I was welcome to join him if I am interested. It was that evening in April 1990 that my "High End Audio baptism" occurred. I returned from that event with a pair of *Mirage* M260 mini-monitors worth 260 dollars, *Beyerdynamic* DT990 Pro headphones for 180 dollars and *Audioquest* speaker cables which cost me my last 60 dollars.

Connecting the speakers to a Japanese *Sansui* integrated amplifier back in Moscow (and subsequently selling the *Bose*) I couldn't even imagine that I would one day be able to tie my whole career to audio for many decades to come.

Meanwhile, reading every audio magazine I could get my hands on cover to cover I was getting absorbed more and more. And to scrutinize them more often I had to make colossal efforts, begging foreign friends who were planning a trip to Russia to bring me a couple of new issues on their way to Moscow (Russian audiophile periodicals started to be published only four years later.)

After a year of perusing the American and British audio press I was ready to assemble my very first real High End Audio system.

I began by renovating my studio apartment in Moscow to convert it into a fully acoustically treated listening room.

Simultaneously I began to develop — unconsciously at first — the main principles of assembling high quality audio systems, although I would be able to formulate them clearly only several years later.

First, as tautological as it may seem at first glance, I understood from the onset of my audio endeavors that *achieving sound of an unusually high quality requires the equipment that is highly unusual in its appearance.*

By 1991 Soviet Union as we know it practically ceased to exist, and the life here started to change dramatically, both politically, and economically. There appeared a lot of new (as a rule still semi-) legal ways to make money. So a year since my first visit to the US I already managed to save enough money to buy my first truly High End Audio system.

My planar magnetic *Apogee Acoustics* "Stage" speakers ($2000 a pair) anchoring my first audiophile installation were fully in line with the above criterion.

The same can be said about the *Sonic Frontiers* SFM-75 tube monoblock amplifier kits (designed by Joe Curcio of *Dynaco* fame) — i.e. full sets of electronic components for Do-It-Yourself assembly ($1695 a pair — assembled by a friend of mine in Moscow for an additional $50), which, compared to the "cool" Japanese equipment of the time, looked like outdated pieces of garbage lab hardware that were thrown out of some local research institute.

Only the source component of that system was quite orthodox in appearance: it was the fairly advanced for the early 90s *Marantz* (*Philips* in Europe) CD-80 player.

The choice of my first High End loudspeakers was largely based on the reviews of **Dick Olsher**, a *Stereophile* author who has firmly gained my trust by then — I have chosen him as one of my mentors at the beginning of my journey in High End Audio. Among the materials written by the magazine's other authors his texts were, for some reason, most congruent with my expectations for the next stage of my path towards the "musical truth."

Several years later during one of the High End Audio shows in the US I finally met Olsher in person. Imagine my surprise when I found out that he worked as a nuclear physicist (my major at MEPhI) at Los Alamos — the official sister city of Chelyabinsk-70 (renamed to Shezhinsk by that point, and home to one of the largest nuclear research facilities in Russia) where I was born and grew up! How can one not believe in coincidences…?

After that I saw, time and time again, that the chains from manufacturers to consumers (including the media's promotion of these products) are always formed following the "like attracts like" principle, i.e. that *internal properties of the products are always fully aligned with the mindset of all of the participants of those chains.*

And finally: I already had a chance to see that auditioning equipment in audio shops only serves to *hinder* productive choice. When I came to the *Sound by Singer* salon in New York to buy *Apogee* "Stage" loudspeakers in August 1991 the salesman offered to audition them with *Krell* amplifiers in one of the demonstration rooms. It was at once clear to me that, had I been basing my purchase decision on a demo like that, I would never have bought them. The converse is also true: all of the equipment I later purchased for myself was bought with no preliminary auditioning but solely following some ideas that I or someone I had considerable trust in had about it.

Thus the meaningless demonstration at Andy Singer's salon did nothing to dispel my deep belief in the accuracy of my decision as I understood fully by then that — although this may seem like a consumer paradox — *the point is not to make the right choice straight away, but to make it right over time.*

The first part of the right decision making always depends on appropriate preparation for it, which is based on inherent common sense, a developed intuition as a result of personal experience and knowledge, but most of all on knowledge base sourced from acknowledged authorities' and experts' opinions; the second is a full awareness of a necessity for the gradual and consistent effort for attaining the right results.

I can still hear those *Apogee* "Stages" when I turned them on at my home for the first time (the intro to the first track on Aaron Neville's *Warm Your Heart* album). Enchantment with the sound produced by that, in essence, fairly basic system, accompanied me in all of my subsequent audiophile adventures, in all of my future relentless attempts to get to "audio nirvana".

That system was, with its relative simplicity, far from perfect, and it took a lot of tweaking on my part to unleash its full potential, but it is true that, as they say, "first impressions are the deepest". Thus, the very first sounds from my very first true High End Audio system that lasted a couple of seconds laid the foundations of my subsequent auditory experiences.

Dick Olsher's 1990 review of these speakers in *Stereophile* had almost nothing in common with what I heard at *Sound by Singer*, the salon which — while being an important part in the respective "chain" in terms of its "internal properties" — also turned out to be the weakest link.

But ten years after buying my first *Apogee* loudspeakers I also bought my (long discontinued) last ones in the same store — so this establishment played a pivotal role for this particular manufacturer to consumer chain and eventually included me as its last link.

And as I would become *Apogee Acoustics'* Russian distributor in just three years, in another *Apogee*-related local chain I would become one of the central links.

FROM NEOPHYTE TO AUDIO MONK

In April of 1992 I have visited the *Stereophile Show* in Los Angeles — the first High End Audio show in my life.

Although I couldn't even imagine any professional activity for myself in audio at the time — with market relations in post-perestroika Russia only beginning to take shape — I nevertheless had some vague commercial intentions and brought along the "Neophyte" phono stage preamplifier manufactured by the extraordinary Russian engineer **Yury Makarov**. Its limited-series production was at that point sponsored (seemingly in a futile hope for some lucrative foreign deals) by certain representatives of the Russian sock-and-stockings "mafia" (whose smug "marketing" instructions I had to endure on the eve of my trip — in the presence of the Creator himself — with feigned attention).

Unfortunately my mission proved completely impossible as the very first flip of the power switch on this truly remarkable in terms of its sound quality device almost electrocuted **Dennis Had**, president of *Cary Audio* (who, upon learning that we can make the unit as OEM for $200 enthusiastically tried to audition it in his demo system). Clutching with one hand the interconnect cable's grounded collar while inserting the cable to his preamp input and also touching its chassis with another, and having been electrically shocked, he immediately felt his enthusiasm dropping to zero[3].

I never felt so much excitement at an audio show either before or after. The show vibe seemed to be on the brink of explosion from the energy it generated in its visitors, and all of the *Stereophile* writers were treated like rock stars while every equipment demonstration was greeted as Revelation.

---

[3] Upon my return to Moscow, Yuri informed me with a straight face that "one has to strictly follow the safety measures at all times."

The stage of expropriating the expropriators in High End Audio has not yet begun, and the price of most equipment that was demonstrated wasn't a stretch for most visitors — and this affordability undoubtedly added to their excitement.

David Manley was demonstrating a system in one of the exhibition's biggest rooms using enormous horn studio monitors and analog master tapes, recorded in his own studio which were played on a professional reel-to-reel tape recorder. *Manley Labs* has not put on a demonstration on that scale ever since. In fact, at most of the subsequent shows that I attended it seemed that the quality of show "demos" was no longer of any importance to them. It appears that *Manley Labs* arrived at the same conclusion I did after a couple of years of being an exhibitor myself: after-show sales are only very vaguely correlated with the "pearls throwing" during the show (although there are *very* rare exceptions to this rule).

David Manley deserves a separate mention not only because of my deepest respect for his numerous talents but also because it was with him that the next stage of my life began.

Immediately after the end of the show David, whom I introduced myself to and briefly chatted with over there, called the house of a friend I was staying with in LA and invited me over to his house in a Los Angeles suburb Chino (pronounced [chee-noh], not [chi-noh], the Manley clan will always be quick to tell you). I took off immediately and arrived at the first audiophile party of my life. Despite the fact that by the time I had arrived all of the guests — including David himself — were considerably drunk the conversations turned out to be incredibly warm and meaningful...

... I will never forget how on my way back from the party, sitting in a car in a God-forsaken part of LA next to a Mexican driver named Umberto who spoke no English and had no idea where we were going I was asking a pimp surrounded with a crowd of transvestite prostitutes and drug dealers how to get to Hollywood Hills. Naturally, that was before mobile phones and GPS (and there was no map in the glove compartment).

There was a lot of good in David but also he was reckless: this, on the one hand, drove him to the creation of the most extraordinary audio "gizmos"[4], on the other gave him no time to think about how that "Russki" will get home in the City of Angels (or Devils, as you prefer).

The dynamics of his life developed according to a similar algorithm: from incredible heights to an abandoned company which only remained afloat thanks to his wife **EveAnna** and son **Luke**. From masterpieces, the peaks of very high-power tube audio technology and professional studio equipment — like the two-storied 300 V Ichiban and the GM-70 power amps or Massive Passive studio mastering processor — to an anonymous life in Paris during his final years when he had to introduce himself with "I am David Manley, yes, *the* David Manley". EveAnna managed to accomplish the impossible: not only to keep all that was best during the years when David was running the company but also bought common sense back into the company's modus operandi — while steadily pursuing its innovations legacy.

When I relayed my impressions from the show to my old university friend **Nikolay Schelok** he begged me to take him and his wife Elena along to my next *Stereophile Show* in San Francisco in May 1993. Unlike the "sock-and-stockings" wheeler dealers, Nikolay was a significantly better educated, far more intelligent and ambitious person — and, giving credit where credit is due, saw the potential to monetize my hobby within the context of up-and-coming prospects

---

[4] Gizmo meaning "(name; proper noun): The good-natured mogwai in Gremlins" according to an apt definition by Harvey Rosenberg, that unforgettable eccentric. The period of the "dizziness from success" of High End Audio in the early 90s was the most appropriate period for audio "gizmology" to thrive, and I have no doubts that David Manley was — probably, without even being aware of it — one of the most outstanding "gizmologists" of the time.

of new political, social and economic developments in Russia that did not even occur to me at that moment.

Nikolay always tried to "grab the bull by the horns", and we became the first "real" Russians in the history of the *Stereophile Show* to visit it — totally unexpectedly for myself! — with professional intentions. Pivotal roles in this were unquestionably played both by my advanced knowledge of the subject and decent English language skills — but also by Nikolay's aggressive business strategy. But still we were treated as lepers, and at the San Francisco show no exhibitor would even consider any sort of cooperation with us.

The only person who immediately reacted to our arrival positively was that same rambunctious David Manley: "Pay up and bring the culture of audio to the masses!" (The 10K in cash, smuggled out of Russia by Nikolay, his wife Elena and myself were paid to him after I picked up a disparate set of amplifiers and preamplifiers right at the factory a few days after the show). That time, his fervor played an entirely positive role in my favor. He also sold us a pair of *Mirage* M1 loudspeakers which he for some reason kept (and which later spent a long time in Yuri Makarov's listening room). After all that he — which was very generous of him — introduced us to **Carl Marchisotto** of *Alon*, saying that his loudspeakers were the best sounding products on the market at the time (which I soon had a chance to make sure of myself).

Manley's vouching for us turned Marchisotto — still on the fence at that point — in our favor. With two American brands willing to work with us we finally secured the opportunity to be taken seriously while offering our services to become the Russian distributors for the other show exhibitors as well.

In the midsummer of 1993 Nikolay, myself and another friend of ours from MIPhE, **Yury Rebedailo**, opened the *Purple Legion* audio store on Kosmodemyanskaya Naberezhnaya in Moscow. I put up a long fight against that name. In my view it is total nonsense. Besides, "Purple Legion" and "Purple Lesion", similar in both writing and pronunciation, shocked many foreigners, when the latter was all they could hear in business meetings. But my partners seemingly could not get enough of Smoke On The Water by Deep Purple so I was ultimately unable to convince them to pick up a different name for the company.

I did not realize it back then but our Kosmodemyanskaya store, existing from 1993 to 1998 at the very peak of the industry, left an indelible impression on the foreigners who came to visit during those years. I remember how **Neil Sinclair**, president of *Theta Digital*, excitedly told me at length how stunned he was after visiting it. Having travelled across America and having seen the shacks and nooks which house the majority of high-end audio salons I realized the scale of our "Stalinist Empire" space with a ceiling height of ten meters: Russians were ahead of the game once again...

From that moment High End Audio became everything to me: both my job and the hobby which allowed me to apply my creativity. We were one of the first distributors of American High End Audio brands in the Russian market so we managed to get the rights to officially represent everything we could have wanted to sell. And *PL* not only became the first proper High End Audio boutique in the country but also presented the most significant product collection under one roof for the years to come — at the very least, of American origin.

Thus I suddenly had everything that I couldn't even had dreamt of a couple years earlier. It was all the more amazing because this opportunity became available to me at the very peak of the global high-performance audio industry's success, during its "golden age".

Throughout many subsequent years I participated in hundreds of audio systems' sales and installations — from the most basic to the most advanced — in the houses and apartments of *PL* customers, while spending all of my free time at home, tweaking and constantly perfecting musical "altars" of my own, travelling from one apogee of my orbit around High End Audio to others, higher, ones. From my first musical altar, built around *Apogee* "Stage" speakers, through their "Studio Grand" system (powered by eight *Manley* single-ended monoblocks with Russian GM-70 direct heated triodes) — to a four-way "active" system based on the top *Apogee* "Grand" loudspeakers (powered by two internal 500 W *Krell* custom amps and two additional external pairs of high-powered *Audio Research* tube amplifiers (MB-600 and MB-210) per stereo channel), which at the time cost several times more than my — still the same one as back in 1991 — Moscow studio apartment turned in an audio monk's cell.

Nevertheless, when my years at *Purple Legion* were still far from numbered, it turned out that the most constant thing in life are changes.

Chapter 5. THE GREAT AUDIOPHILE TRAGEDY

VIDEO KILLED THE AUDIO STARS

The arrival of the compact disc in 1982 had an immensely powerful impact on the whole audio industry. Although many first-rate vinyl record players (*Linn, VPI* and others) existed at the time, and the sound of the first CDs — despite its *"Perfect sound forever"* slogan — still raised many doubts, the market hailed the arrival of a new audio format as the Third Coming, and CD remains to this day the most commercially successful format in the history of audio.

The overall sales across the whole range of audio equipment rose dramatically across the world, and the list of new commercially available equipment significantly expanded as well.

The steadfast economic growth in the West, the defeat of Eastern Bloc countries in the Cold War, the opening of new internal and external markets, the availability of cheap labor in China, stable development of the music business and a young generation that still believed in music as a religion allowed for the demand, which for twenty years — from the early 1970s — spurred the rising interest in audio equipment of the highest quality to solidify.

Yet the foundations of "pure audio's" well-being were shaken in 1996 with the large-scale economic crisis that began in South-East Asia (where a large proportion of High End Audio equipment has always been sold) and then spread to the rest of the world.

Reaching its peak by 1996–1997, the High End Audio market began to gradually enter a stage of stagnation which lasted until around 2005 and was then followed by the eventual decrease of sales for almost every company that was actively involved in it, pushing the vast majority of them into the state of the deepest recession.

The market's "temperature" during a previous year is most easily measured by the level of the stars that performed at the dealer reception organized every January by the American enterprise *Monster (Cable)* in enormous banquet halls of Las Vegas' most famous hotels for the thousands of *CES* visitors. While, during the industry's best years Stevie Wonder, Rod Stewart, Earth, Wind & Fire, Carlos Santana and other superstars performed at the event, at the last such event in 2016 it were The Jacksons ("4") who performed at it — although, to be fair, even in its best years *Monster* would hardly be able to afford the fifth member of that band.

The economic crisis of late 1990s also had a decisive influence on the radical strategy changes implemented by the leading manufacturers of the Consumer Electronics industry, who were faced with having to choose a path for their future development.

At the turn of the century new digital audio and video formats were being developed simultaneously, they were supposed to replace CDs as well as analog video cassettes and Laser Disks, and the Consumer Electronics industry found itself at the crossroads, it had to decide where to invest its main resources.

In those years *Sony* and *Philips* continued to organize demonstrations of their new multichannel sound format, "Super

Audio Compact Disc" (SACD), defining their vision for future development — towards the improvement of music, not video, reproduction.

At the same time the alliance of manufacturers called "DVD Alliance", under the auspices of *Toshiba* and the largest video content owner of the time, *Warner Brothers*, announced the creation of a new video storage medium, capable of supporting the newly created television format, HDTV. As a result of political and economic decisions, music was pushed to the side, and the vast majority of the industry's R&D and production resources were thrown into the development and commercial implementation of new video technologies.

It was primarily for this reason that the last twenty years saw no significant changes in commonly adopted consumer sound recording/reproduction technologies (multiple new ways of digital music distribution notwithstanding).

Back in the mid-1990s the presence of consumer electronic products in a household was reduced to a landline telephone, a TV set and a music system. No one could have dreamt of a home cinema, smartphones, expensive portable audio or video gear, etc., and consumers systematically spent considerable amounts of money on "pure" stereo home equipment.

The dominant technology of video cassette recording did not allow to get a high image quality on anything larger than an average-sized TV screen. The arrival of DVD and HDTV at the end of the 1990s, which suddenly allowed to significantly improve the quality of video images and drastically increase screen sizes, immediately pushed the manufacturers of quality music equipment to the side and gave center stage to entirely new players (*sic!*).

Not like in audio industry, the giant leaps and bounds in the progress of video equipment was largely related to all-encompassing, exhaustive and commonly accepted consumer image quality standards which facilitated the emergence of far more productive new development vectors and image quality criteria.

Just as — as the *Buggles* sang back in 1979, "*...video killed the radio stars...*", video murdered audio in exactly the same way, pushing it to the curb of technological development and throwing it into the abyss of thoughtless running around in circles in an endless, entirely pointless "arms race".

At first, most consumer audio equipment manufacturers swallowed the bait of promised sales increases, kindly offered to them by the *home theater* concept that arrived aboard a new multimedia technological revolution. Their reasoning was as follows: it is always better to sell three pairs of speakers rather than one or three two-channel amps instead of one (not to mention — for those who could endure it — a surround sound processor for good measure).

However, this strategy ultimately played a cruel joke with High End Audio, as small manufacturers would never be able to compete against large corporations who use ever changing features in their products mostly as a means to defeat their competitors.

The appearance of **DVD** and **HDTV** took the High End Audio industry off guard. Along with a drop in sales, caused by the outbreak of a global economic crisis, albeit temporary, the sudden turn of global overall consumer electronics industry's marketing policies towards new video technologies and home cinema left many of them no time to contemplate their future development strategies.

Mark Fisher, editor of *The Absolute Sound* at the time, has a different opinion on the issue. In the interview I conducted with him in Moscow for *Audiomagazin* in 2009 he stated:

"A decline began at the end of the 90s, and a fairly dramatic one at that. Two-channel audio systems were replaced with audio/video installations more and more, so the market became, for the most part, multi-channel, and began to be flooded with vast amounts of mediocre equipment. The vast majority of high-performance stereo manufacturers withdrew from the multi-channel market segment. Many simply didn't believe that one could attain sound quality comparable to a decent stereo system within the confines of a multi-channel system. This arrogance and refusal to accept something new were the causes of the collapse. Today, most of them admit that it was a fatal mistake: they surrendered their positions to large companies, whose products often left a lot to be desired, instead of attempting to bring the traditions and culture of High End Stereo to the multi-channel segment. As a result, early adopters of home cinema, lacking choice, were forced to contend with 'cheap' — in all senses of the word — *Sony* and *Pioneer* receivers, as well as their speakers. People were buying what they were seeing on the shelves, which is only natural. And real High End Audio, sort of, retreated to the underground.

This was the fault of high quality stereo equipment manufacturers who abandoned their clientele during a difficult period of transition. Not so much because of financial limitations, but because of arrogance, lack of faith and simple snobbery, they turned their backs on the new technologies. Insulating themselves in their tiny world, and voluntarily giving up attempts to stop the market degradation, they believed that a small part of the audience, which would continue to purchase their limited-series expensive products, would suffice. But they miscalculated, not getting even a fraction of what they had hoped for. Moreover, as a result of the arising information void in terms of High End Audio, the number of potential buyers of quality equipment among the grownup younger generation drastically decreased as well, so that generational continuity was broken."

Actually, as I see it, very few High End Audio companies were able to resist the temptation to fritter away their efforts and resources on the development of home cinema components. As events that followed showed, on the opposite, the ones who resisted that temptation were the ultimate winners. Because they were unable to reverse the trend of falling "pure" stereo sales, competing with large corporations (despite some sporadic additional sales in the home cinema segment) and wasting colossal resources — particularly at surround sound processors' R&D and production — was what ultimately sank the companies "seduced" by Home Theatre.

I once bumped into Dan D'Agostino from *Krell* in the elevator of the Las Vegas *Mirage,* where they had a demo suit during that year's CES show (at that time *Krell* was showing every symptom of the impending serious problems). Using the chance, I asked him: "Dan, you were taking too many chances with your attempts to get into the home cinema business, weren't you?'. "Yes, that was our biggest mistake," he replied (by the way, the executive board of the company he founded fired him soon after this conversation with the help of its new investors).

The arrival of DVD (and Home Theatre that accompanied it) was only the first sign (or rather the first harbinger) of changes that appeared on the — still cloudless at the time — horizon of "pure" audio.

Unfortunately, some much worse global changes affecting High End Audio's future perspectives had yet to occur...

A MAN IS KNOWN BY THE AUDIO SYSTEM COMPANY HE KEEPS

The mid-1990s era, which can truly be called the Golden Age of High End Audio, was relegated to history. Today, as I am writing this book, the "golden" age has given way to a… let's call it a "silicon" one.

The fact that, by the end of the 2000s the industry will gradually begin hitting a dead end, is largely a result of the development vector that it chose at the height of its success as well as the dominant nature of the links in the aforementioned chains from manufacturer to customer, which formed under the influence of that vector. Consequently, it ended up in a state which is best described using the words of Norman Lebrecht: "As the Titanic was sinking, the orchestra still continued to play."[1]

This does not only refer to the properties of the audio equipment itself but the value system that it embodies, changing, in the blink of an eye, with global social, political, economic and cultural transformation of that period.

The veteran audio journalist Ken Kessler told me in my interview with him for *Audiomagazin*: "The history of High End Audio is not cloudless, and I am inclined to view it not just through the prism of the changes in the 'hardware' itself but in terms of the customers' shifting attitudes towards it."

The first wave of audiophiles, properly educated and engaged in some form of productive activity, with music being at the top of their list of priorities, gave way to the new generation X by the mid-90s: young and mercantile pushy yuppies[2], who were making money out of thin air.

---

[1] N. Lebrecht. *Maestros, Masterpieces and Madness: The Secret Life and Shameful Death of the Classical Record Industry.*

[2] Yuppies (short for "Young Urban Professional Person") — a demographic phenomenon that originated in the US in late 1980s, producing young business executives who openly espoused material values.

This very air of emptiness and primitive commercialism began to fill the profile of the products they demanded. Audio was no exception. As they say, "he who pays the piper calls the tune" (in this case, quite literally).

The chief paradox of my professional life in High End Audio has always been that the products I saw as having the most valuable essence were always in the least demand — and, conversely, products that "I would never touch with a long stick", as they were lacking any substantial content, enjoyed the most widespread consumer demand (although if you think about it in the context of all the aforementioned new social trends it's not really a paradox).

Both technical and aesthetic aspects of audio components' sound quality are always tied not only with their own objective internal properties, but also with the subjective "internal properties" of all participants of the corresponding chains of production, distribution, media support, sales and installation outlets and, ultimately, the customers themselves. The latter are able to generate a new chain through a feedback loop of sorts connecting manufacturers to new customers whom the old ones can infect with their own eenthusiasm for a given product.

As in other instances of high-priority life choices (and in the case of High End Audio, that's what it is supposed to be), the current state of affairs can be described with a slightly altered old adage: "a man is known by the sound system he keeps."

It is remarkable how closely the peculiar mentality of a given dedicated customer correlate with the specifics of, say, the loudspeakers that he or she prefers. I am exaggerating somewhat, of course, but still I can't help noticing time after time that the narrowness of the sound radiation pattern, sonic resolution and "micro-dynamic shadings" of the sound of typical horn loaded loudspeakers very often go hand in hand with the narrowness of their owners' musical outlook; and on the other hand the "openness" of the sound of some exotic planar magnetic transducers such as *Magnepan* is usually accompanied with their typical owners' open-mindedness and breadth of musical interests.

The same quasi-paradox of consumer preferences also manifests itself in audio boutiques' survival of the fittest race. I remember visiting **Christopher Hansen** Beverly Hills store back in 1992, with its incredible listening rooms, one of them specially set up for the demonstration of *Apogee* "Grand" loudspeakers. It was a large room with wavy ceilings and, naturally, acoustically calibrated, situated inside a meticulously finished, impressively large establishment with fountains adorning its entrance, spacious halls, complete with flower-filled vases and other pretty attributes. Yet just two years after my visit it was forced to shut down (as did most of salons like this one, that laid a claim to the "absolute" — in terms of their aspirations to demonstrate equipment in absolutely flawless conditions).

Meanwhile, they were easily outlasted by audio joints of all kinds located in slums and basements, where, in order to audition some gear, one had to move a coffee table littered with remains of booze and snacks.

Unlike the restaurant business where the visitor enters into a monetary relationship with the establishment at the moment of having ordered the food potential clients of audio salons always took it for granted that they could, figuratively speaking, order everything on the auditioning "menu", put their feet up on the table, "suck the dealer's blood" as much as they please and finally, without getting the bill or even thanking anybody, just get up and simply leave. Naturally, this business model proved entirely unviable, especially when demand for audio equipment began to gradually falter.

In terms of whom to blame for deteriorating audio shops conditions — the stuff policy or the ungrateful customers — it's like "what came first, the chicken or the egg" debate, especially because unlike previous generations of well-educated and good mannered true sound enthusiasts the vast majority of customers in the late 90s judged everything and everyone by themselves. Thus, if they subsisted through, to put it mildly, misleading people twenty four hours a day (in the spirit of the times), they had no doubt that everyone else was doing exactly the same. There was absolutely no trust to the store stuff's expertise and no thoughts of supporting the stores on their mind. Even the demonstration of a certain level of technical competence by an audio salon employee could go down poorly with clients like these: a large part of them saw it as an instrument of deception and exploitation of knowledge and experience in order to harm, not help, customers who clearly lack technical savvy.

It is lamentable that throughout the years of my professional activity in Russia (even taking the specifics of that moment in our history — just after the demise of the USSR — and the corresponding local atmosphere of "primary accumulation of capital" into account), I have seen all kinds of swindlers, con men, thieves and thugs of the domestic variety among my clientele while the number of "civilized" law obeying citizens, engaged in productive, socially beneficial activity and buying the quite expensive High End equipment thoughtfully can be counted on the fingers of two hands if not one. That is why "he who pays the piper calls the tune" correlation thoughts are unfortunately unavoidable.

High End Audio's esthetic content description cannot be fully "digitized" as its objective technical one and its transmission is only possible through direct and sincere human contact. The main purpose of audio salons lay precisely in creating an atmosphere conducive to forming such mutual trust relationships and in that sense audio salons were meant to be "temples" of Music (and audio, as its trusted servant). But in reality, given the lack of a need for High Art among the customers of the time and, what's more, the lack of trust between the parties involved, relationships at such establishments began to gradually deteriorate across the board, down to the point of totally unproductive mercantile flea-market squabbles.

Krell was once among the largest and successful High End Audio companies (which is why I bring it up as much as I do). During one of our last brief conversations I have asked its founder, Dan D'Agostino, another rhetorical question: "Dan, don't you think it is ironic that we have ultimately found ourselves in a position of having to appeal to those who do not really care about what we're actually trying to achieve?" He looked at me intently and, after a short pause, replied: "Yes, unfortunately, you're right."

The path a large part of high-quality equipment manufacturers chose at the turn of century is evident, and it reflected the spirit of the times to come. Having begun to tempt the "fat wallets" with nothing more than status symbols, they gradually moved away from the production of delicate instruments for exploring musical reality to the manufacturing of "audio jewelry."

And because you cannot wear your speakers on your wrist like a watch all the principal players in the industries began — with destructive consequences both for consumers and, ultimately, themselves — trying to "have their cake and eat it": to make lofty statements with very meaningful looks on the one hand and dance to the expropriators' tune on the other.

Yielding to the wishes of the consumers who were uneducated and limited in their understanding of High End Audio's main mission, the industry little by little was losing awareness of its main signposts in the early 2000s.

Which gradually lead it to the brink of the precipice.

SONIC WALLPAPER

The overall value of entire musical heritage can be represented as a system of interconnected artistic "tanks" (representing different genres) with constantly changing social relevance of the each "tank's" individual content. As in every self-contained system at any given moment, in a total system of musical outputs of all kinds, according to the law of communicating vessels we all have learned in school, if the concentration of the musical content value increase in some of the "tanks", it has to decrease at others — and vice versa.

Audio equipment of the highest quality has to serve the need for a search for the "tanks" with the highest concentration of musical content value and the need for the highest level of its appreciation. Obviously, the maximum depth of musical content value representation, i.e. the depth of its resolution, is a prerequisite to achieve this goal. While the widest breadth of the content choice can fully support the mission, it can do this only if it preserves the content value's maximum resolution; however, if it's achieved at the cost of diminishing the resolution, then it can be only an obstacle on the way to reach High End Audio's main goals.

In the global Zeitgeist of the Millennium when consumers went berserk over quantity of stuff they craved versus its quality, it was no accident that the undisputed leader of the next generation of consumer electronics, *Apple,* began its onslaught on the music and consumer electronics markets by decreasing the resolution — from the Compact Disc's specifications, already in need of improvement, to a compressed format of an even lower quality, MP3. The latter was developed according to the key priorities consonant with the new generation of music lovers: as much download and storage capacity as possible and maximum interface usability. That is, widest breadth of the available content choice and maximal convenience of access to it at the (unavoidable for that moment technologically) cost of lowering the depth of the available content's resolution.

> Ken Kessler lamented in my interview with him: "Take my own sixteen-year-old son, for instance. How many times have I offered him a decent audio system! But it does not connect to the Internet, has no video games, no hundreds of FM stations, you cannot carry it around in your pocket. And my son adores music, he is a true music lover! But for a young man, brought up in a virtual environment, on MP3 and portable players with headphones, his reality is computer animation, chats and the Web. And the music should correspond to that. So why would he need High End Audio?"

Thanks to considerable technological progress, over the last twenty years the bit rate of downloadable music on most platform increased considerably, and not only matched the quality of CD, but even surpassed it, not to mention that the most of the newest streaming services like *Tidal* and *Qobuz* can stream true *hi-res* audio in real time. Nevertheless, even presuming that this achievement is the result of a long term strategy to eventually provide the best sound quality available, because of its colossal influence on music consumption across the world during that initial period of 2000s, *Apple* managed to re-direct the overall vector of future audio technology development from sound quality as the main priority to maximum quantity, i.e. convenient and easy access to the almost limitless number of recordings.

And, in that sense, during its "Second Coming", *Apple, Inc.* delivered the knockout punch to High End Audio's prospects for steady future development.

Nevertheless, despite the increasing gap between High End Audio and the main developments in not only technology, but also social trends, a good example of the opposite approach was provided by the leading Consumer Electronics company of the previous generation, *Sony*, which, unlike many of its competitors, has always fought for the most up-to-date technological solutions of the highest possible content delivery quality.

Apart from the famous case of *Sony*'s failed attempt to defeat the inherently inferior VHS cassette format with its cutting-edge Beta format (featuring among its many advantages a much better sound quality) I also remember how impressed I was with the sound of their top-tier "pure" stereo system featuring electrostatic loudspeakers in Los Angeles back in 1992 (designated as SS-R10, worth incredible — for the time — $12 000).

Even given its current haggard state in consumer electronics segment, *Sony* is still trying to release products of the highest content delivery quality. And the myth — cultivated over many years — that the co-founder of the company, Akio Morita, set the capacity limit of the CD exactly as the length of Beethoven's 9th Symphony, his favorite piece of music, indicates that things could be entirely different in the world of consumer electronics and that even the industry's leaders can still prioritize sound quality when developing their company's mission. Moreover, back in its day *Sony* dominated the market as unquestionably as *Apple* does today, and even just before 2000s when the priorities of a vast majority of music lovers began to be purposefully shifted "from quality to quantity" by all the large CE corporations.

To reiterate, even if this was a part of the all-encompassing long term plan of building a "Brave New Digital World", nevertheless, in those first years of its implementation instead of creating the best conditions possible for the conscious search for deep musical meanings (and the highest sound quality is a necessary prerequisite to the vast majority of listeners for developing their music appreciation skills), by worsening the most widely distributed musical content's sonic properties (which hinders listeners' personal growth in those skills), the CE big players were making music lovers to use the taps of the "tanks" with the most diluted, in terms of its value, musical content, often watered down to a point of nothing more than plain "sonic wallpaper."

WHEN THE FUTURE CONSTANTLY REMAINS IN THE PAST

In January 1994 the *Stereophile* magazine put a photo of a *Krell* amplifier on the cover, it represented the biggest achievements of solid-state audio technology of the time, and next to it — of the *Cary Audio* single-ended direct heated triode amplifier, a carbon copy of similar amps from the 1930s. The headline read: "If one of these amplifiers is RIGHT, the other must be WRONG." Nevertheless, reviews of both amplifiers turned out to be glorious. And not because the magazine had already completely sold out to its advertisers by that point and the final verdict lay far outside of its jurisdiction. Rather, because of the question that is "in the air" to this day, namely: how can it be that ancient equipment can still demonstrate not just comparable but, in certain aspects, even a higher sound quality than the most modern one?

And why does the future of audio constantly remain in the past?

Could it be that, in terms of sound quality, *simple things used to be made well* and now *complicated things are made poorly*? ...

Here, we return to the notorious issue of lack of any precisely defined and commonly accepted sound quality standards in audio. I have no doubts that precisely because of this, applying mostly audio's aesthetic techniques can yield sonic results fully comparable with sonic results obtained with a help of its most up do date technologies.

There is no doubt that without strictly following clear and commonly accepted standards along the whole signal chain of video equipment from the studio cameras to TV receivers (and without full availability of all the necessary adjustments), we would never have the opportunity to behold the "Brave New World of Digital Television" today.

Unlike the situation with video equipment the issue with audio technology lies in the fact that, given the absence of a comprehensive system of sound quality standards, it is not only the customers who are unsure of what they are buying but the audio manufacturers and all their intermediaries themselves are not really sure of what they are making, reviewing and selling.

That is why, unfortunately, in the field of dedicated audio equipment someone could attach a couple of low-resolution horn loaded drivers designed for a completely different — let's say, Public Address — application to a meticulously polished, made out of expensive wood, monument to human vanity and folly — and would still be taken seriously by those around him. Such nonsense would never fly in the video world.

This cognitive dissonance of having inconsistent thoughts, believes or attitudes, the main source of the infamous *audiophilia nervosa*, is easily seen in the differences between the styles of typical reviews of audio and video equipment. Here we are:

VIDEO	AUDIO
"... but all the aforementioned <technical> issues were too obvious and happened too frequently for us to be able to recommend this 3D-television to be used as the primary videophile display."	*"Considering that the user gets all these capabilities, the 'Quad 99 CDP-2' CD player is simply screaming in your face: BUY ME! Or, at the very least, LISTEN TO ME!"*
(WIDESCREEN REVIEW, ISSUE 153, JANUARY 2011, P. 25, REVIEW OF TOSHIBA LED/ LCD VIDEO SCREEN)	(STEREOPHILE, JANUARY 2006, P. 109)
	"Oh, not just for <the magazine's readers> — <the reviewer's wife> replied. — I think that all should listen to these speakers, as they can offer something to EVERYONE. I agree with this assessment. You must go and listen for yourself."
	(THE ABSOLUTE SOUND, JANUARY 2011, P. 167 — A QUOTE FROM THE REVIEW OF "CARMEL" LOUDSPEAKERS BY YG ACOUSTICS)

It is crucial to note here, that the quality of video images is evaluated only in terms of its conformity to an established standard and nothing more, i.e. no one claims to have achieved the full conformity of the image on the screen to some *concentrated gaze looking at the real world events*. While in audio in the absence of accepted sound quality standards a critical listener is forced to skip the stage of evaluation of sound reproduction quality per se with all of its specifics, which should be described on its own by the appropriate set of standards — instead having to apply the method of juxtaposing the demonstrated sound quality to some abstract "live" sound. This methodology requires the description of an audio system's actual sound quality to be subjectively "embellished" with a whole arsenal of flowery, exaggerated and exalted prose (see above).

Andy Singer, one of America's most distinguished High End Audio dealers, who owned the world-famous *Sound by Singer* salon in Manhattan for many years, complained in our 2008 interview for *Audiomagazin* about the worst strategy possible that our industry chose. Picking the path of least resistance and giving in to those with money, it delegated the power of equipment choice to neophyte customers.

As a result of the absence of objective consumer sound quality standards, instead of truly educating consumers, "dragging them up by the collar", the High End Audio industry has instead started to grovel in front of them, descending on the most basic level of communication when promoting its products. What's more, not without the help of the modern specialized media — mostly pleasing the advertisers, not readers and urging the latter that they "must go and listen" for themselves — the expertise of the dealers became degraded in the eyes of the customers, and as a result of it, when they do "go and listen" — *what* must they listen to exactly?!

I am sure that the vast majority of them will be very confused when they are pressed to answer this question.

With no objective sound quality standards, is there a way to clearly describe the sonic difference between, say, a high-end ribbon tweeter of the highest resolution and a mediocre horn loaded one (by the way, originally intended for a different purpose entirely)? Moreover, when I claim that all parameters of the video signal chain are "standardized" and regret the sad fact that we don't have the same situation in audio, I do not only mean that we will then be able to progressively improve the commonly established level of sound quality. One of the reasons I bring it up here once again is that the *i*-generation insists on a quantitative approach to all kinds of quality, including the quality of sound. Because of that, the lack of commonly accepted sound quality standards further exacerbates the negative forecast for the continued interest in high performance audio.

As mentioned many times before, High End Audio is located at the intersection of technology and art. Art builds its effect upon the *contrast* with reality, not its *hyper conformity* with it. That is why it is subjective and that is why there is always something to discuss on the Internet in the context of *opinions*. The technical aspect, however, is entirely objective and has to fit within the framework of established technical and scientific concepts and the standards that have been developed with their help. Here, too, we have something to discuss on the Internet, but now in the context of *knowledge*. An attempt to mix everything together — say, apples and beefsteaks — leads to the fundamental cognitive impediment in High End Audio: a lack of commonly accepted truths and a unified institution of authority. Which can lead to the worst of all: a zero level of trust between all the parties involved.

The art aspect within high-performance audio is, naturally, not conducive to developing a single set of quality standards, but its continued presence at the foundation of High End Audio is a direct consequence of their absence. I see no tragedy in parting with this aspect while devising comprehensive consumer audio standards akin to their video counterparts. On the contrary: "grounding" audio in the firm foundation of standardization would only induce its next boom.

The main obstacle to developing sound quality standards, necessary for audio today, lies not in technical issues and the disparate array of existing concepts and ideas, but in opposition *within the industry itself*: as the vast majority of contemporary manufacturers (especially of analog equipment) will, without a doubt, be left out. And what will they do then?!

In ancient "three-beam" CRT projectors in order to ensure their proper functioning the design had a whole range of various installation stages and calibrations, specific to this particular type of devices and mostly irrelevant for modern matrix projectors. Similarly, various types of speakers or amplifiers have particularities that, ideally, should be analyzed — and possibly standardized — using methods that are specific to a given equipment type. As a result of this approach, the procedure of equipment testing and setting up, given overall *meta*-standards, can have components specific to the "genre", without which these tests and installation procedures would be insufficient, but which would allow the types of a given component to be brought to some kind of a common denominator. A lack of standards — both meta and those adapted to every "genre" of audio equipment — is, in my view, the key reason for High End Audio's stagnation and decay.

Using video as an analogy and considering the latest achievements in measurement technology, one can state with all certainty that most of these ideas lie at the surface and could be easily implemented. For example, some of such basic parameters could be: optimal application fields, overall sonic resolution, overall sound dynamic range, sound "gray scale" linear level tracking, fixed amplitude and dynamic transfer functions of proper timbre reproduction.

But these standards can only be generated from the top, i.e. through specialized associations, public organizations and state institutions (all the initiatives to form such institutions within the global High End Audio industry inevitably failed). This will never happen at the level of separate companies as my former compatriot **Vladimir Lamm**, the owner of the extraordinary New York company *Lamm Industries, Inc,* once shared in a private conversation: "Listen, I've been using all of these special measurement techniques in my own designs for years but I cannot say that openly — should large companies hear about it and begin using it, what would happen to my own business?"

His words are supported by a plethora of indisputable facts and observations. Take the video industry, for instance, which has commonly accepted standards, but there are no manufacturers who employ just several person (like *Lamm Industries*) or even ten times more employees (except for some private installers).

It is precisely because of the lack of commonly accepted sound quality standards that the future of audio constantly remains in the past (with the possible exception of the most advanced digital equipment). Accordingly, as a result of the absence of steady improvements in sound quality within the audio industry the vast majority of customers see no point in replacing old equipment with the new one. And they are quite right: a large amount of analog audio equipment being made today significantly exceeds analogous (*sic!*) models made years ago in price, but is usually of a lower quality (at a certain price point and with the appropriate deflation related correction).

This is why the huge slagheaps of decent second-hand audio equipment that is fully functional and still easily available on the used market (unlike any other home appliance, which sooner or later always ends up as garbage) keep growing.

This is one of the main explanations for the lack of not only new sales but also any further progressive development of the industry.

While everyone is constantly replacing old phones, TV sets and other gadgets because their quality (at a given price) is constantly increasing, "dedicated" audio equipment is usually a once-in-a-lifetime purchase for most customers. And, considering constant changes in the specifics of demand and almost complete absence of an adaptation to it on the part of today's audio industry, where are new sales supposed to come from?!

The history of television broadcasting exhaustively illustrates that innovation requires us to first decide which parameters we want to improve and then to *simply get down to improving them*. Without an objective foundation for sound quality evaluation and commonly accepted standards the high performance audio business has turned into a fruitless "polishing of old steam engines."

With all due respect towards the vinyl records' legacy the latest burst of interest towards this format is, to me, one of the best proofs of the last statement. Would it occur to anyone to bring from a junk yard and watch a television set from the 1960s — the age of vinyl's domination — today, and then to place a magnifying lens filled with tap water in front of it to watch it (let alone, to argue with other Internet forum dwellers about which kind of water to fill it with)? The firmly established audiophile notion that it has lately become much easier to accept the shortcomings of the digital medium than the imperfections of analog one (e.g. vinyl records, all sorts of magnetic tapes, etc), against the interests of fans of good music, has been completely surpassed by a marketing onslaught and "political correctness" — when many journalists can't voice their private opinions in order to keep their jobs, awaiting a more opportune moment in the future, it seems.

Which is — for this exact reason as well — still not arriving.

BETWEEN CREDENT VERBO AND NULLIUS IN VERBA

The motto of one of the first academies of science, the Royal Society in London, in Latin reads *Nullius in verba*, which roughly translates to "take nobody's word for anything." The unceasing and intensive growth of the body of knowledge during the Enlightenment, so dissimilar to the traditional systems of beliefs within the contexts of already established institutions, mostly of religious kind, required fundamental, total criticism, the break with the previous order of things.

It took considerable time and the establishment of the absolutely new scientific environment for the different motto that reappeared from the past as if on a spiral coil — to become relevant again. *Credent verbo*, i.e. "trust in the word" — but this time a new, *scientific*, one.

Nowadays, when knowledgeable and experienced audio dealers are being put six feet under one after the other, the information on such a phenomenon as High End Audio is increasingly becoming fragmented and distorted — it is usually sourced from the Internet publications of various degrees of anonymousness. In the old-fashioned lingo reliability of such information sources was described by "hearing it through the grapevine' expression.

The gloating on specialized forums over audio dealers' and distributors' demise — "they got what they deserved" — is usually based on a certain number of *bad* examples (when, for instance, a demonstration of an audio system worth 250 thousand Euros employs a scratched CD that get stuck every 30 seconds, and no one bats an eye) from which *bad conclusions* are immediately drawn.

Throughout my quarter of a century professional career in High End Audio I have never seen myself as just a dealer or a distributor. My personal experiences compelled me to play "both sides of the board", which made me sincerely try to correct mistakes on both sides of the "sales counter barricades." As early as the mid-90s my writings began to be appear regularly in local audio press and general publications. My main motivation was not only to present general information about High End Audio and to report on its current affairs but also to erect bridges of mutual understanding between all the parties involved, be it professionals or laymen, who were — surprisingly — divided and often entirely incapable of finding a common ground.

To avoid "hearing it through the grapevine" I always tried to get my information from the most immediate source whether that source were manufacturers, equipment designers, record producers or key figures in audio journalism, who were witnesses of the industry's evolution from its very inception.

Caribbean Sea cruises, organized by **Gary Reber** of the *Widescreen Review* magazine in the 2003 and 2005, gave me a chance to meet many significant record producers and audio engineers, and this communication is never an essential part of your business if your goal is simply to sell expensive hardware. You can do that easily without witnessing **Alan Parsons** tell stories about working on *The Beatles* and *Pink Floyd* albums, **Phil Ramone** spinning tales about Frank Sinatra's recordings, **Elliott Scheiner** reminiscing about his work on *Steely Dan* albums and the ups and downs of the multichannel remixing of *Queens' The Night At the Opera*, and **Al Schmitt** sharing his secrets of recording an orchestra for Diana Krall's releases. Nevertheless, I never looked for shortcuts in my life, and to make sure that the core values of my professional career in High End Audio are intact I had to gain as many experiences like these as possible.

While working on a series of interviews with prominent record producers for *Audiomagazin* in 2006 I flew to Nashville for the interview with **George Massenburg**, who was working at the time at one of the top recording studios in the US, *Blackbird*. There in one of the studio's control rooms I played to George Aaron Neville's *Warm Your Heart* album — he co-produced with Linda Ronstadt — thus coming full circle in my twenty-plus year-long audiophile passion: it was this very album that I played first on my first truly audiophile system with *Apogee* "Stage" speakers brought back to Moscow from New York back in 1991[3] — and now I was listening to the album with its co-producer in a control room of one of the best studios in the world.

To this day that record remains a benchmark for me in terms of both its sound quality and its musical content, never mind its place in my audiophile biography. As they say "you never forget your first love"...

My verdict, voiced to George, was: "Phew, thank God! I haven't lived in vain. On truly audiophile systems this recording would sound to me even more expressive and meaningful than here, in the control room of one of the best US recording studios." George didn't even argue with me — and not just because he didn't think it was necessary: I guess he is fully aware of the possible shortcomings of the studio environment. The limitations of cheap professional CD player, the lack of any claims for "absolute" of the studio amplifiers, not to mention the sound quality limitations of the horn control monitors (moreover, built into the wall) were too apparent to any seasoned audiophile.

A visit to *Blackbird* allowed me to make some interesting observations. As I was sitting at the mixing desk listening to the main control monitors I have noticed that the ubiquitous *Yamaha*

---

[3] As an example of possible contradictions within the music appreciation circles George told me that when Neville's managers heard the mastered album for the first time, they didn't like it so much that "they wanted to kill him."

NS-10 near field studio monitors adjacent to it were connected to the power amplifier with a very expensive *Nordost* loudspeaker cable (worth thousands of dollars). I asked George; "What made the studio owners to use it?" He replied to me that "People come here to realize their wildest dreams." I have replied: "Even though audiophiles and recording professionals are supposed to share the same core ideas regarding obtaining the best sound quality we often borrow from each other the most superficial and the least appropriate ones. It seems like some recording professionals think of audiophiles just as buyers of cables for thousands of dollars, while some audiophiles trusting you, professionals, to know better, blindly embrace recording studio equipment like horn loudspeakers, which were actually developed for radically different environment and application than typical audiophile ones."

During visiting the studio I got another proof that the professional recording environment — not unlike any other industrial facility — is not the best place for aesthetic exercises in search of the last remaining nuances of the musical truth. This puzzles many people who think that, by definition, the ultimate reference for quality evaluation of the sound they will get at their home is the sound of the track when it's reproduced through control monitors in the studio where it was mastered. My visit to *Blackbird* confirmed a different position: while it's true that the information recorded on the final consumer product is definitely inferior compared to the information recorded on the studio first generation master, nevertheless, when reproduced through the best audiophile domestic systems, their sonic superiority to the typical professional studio gear with its imperfect installation can sometimes outweigh the obvious deficiencies of consumer music software. So during my visit to the Nashville studio I had another proof that under best circumstances home High End Audio systems are capable of making discernible even more musically significant information than you can hear in a control room of a typical studio from a master; even if a commercially released medium is less rich in recorded nuances.

When I met **Marc Almond**, a British singer, in 1999 I already had several Russian musical projects to my name as an executive producer, the most notable was **Alla Bayanova**'s album *Fly, My Song,* where she singing to the music performed by a number of outstanding musicians led by the pianist extraordinaire **Mikhail Aptekman**.

That record played the decisive role when I offered Marc to record a "Russian" album. First Marc was clearly perplexed by my offer. But after enjoying Alla's record he called me from London to say that "OK, let's do it!"

In a subsequent review in a British newspaper the *Heart On Snow* album (2003) earned a five-star rating. The latest album by Britney Spears was awarded three stars in the same issue, a remaster of a Beatles record — four. That review also included the passage that "one should not expect an album like this within the next twenty years" (twenty years later one can see that the prediction came true). Almond himself still considers that record to be one of his greatest accomplishments.

The work on my own producing projects allowed me to see the sound recording process from the inside and gain experience at all stages of music creation: from artist and repertoire selection through making decisions and recording arrangements in the studio, where one sees recording engineers and producers in action and hears what "professional" sound with all of its advantages and drawbacks really is — to the mastering stage as the record takes on its final sound. This period of my life expanded my audiophile outlook immensely and taught me "to separate the grain from the chaff", defining recorded artefacts and discerning them from playback distortions.

I mention some of my achievements here only to show that the right to *one's own opinion* does not come out of thin air of empty arrogance or sudden appearance of technological means for its propagation. There is only one way of earning it — by making a considerable and purposeful effort to do so.

Unfortunately, what we observe today in the field of information distribution and exchange (particularly, in relation to high performance audio) can be described by changing this section's title to its opposite: from the positive *Credent verbo*, based on valuable opinions of recognized experts at the peak of High End Audio in the 1990s — to the negative *Nullius in verba* of the recently arrived age of the Internet.

Undoubtedly the ability to discuss any topic on the Internet is a huge achievement of our civilization but there are two sides to every coin. Because of previously unimaginable level of information "noise", the demand for expert opinions, given the universal unfounded certainty in the possession of relevant knowledge, only increases. With information being spread over the Internet with no obstacles experts are simply unable to "shout through the noise" made by the crowd of laymen swelling from a sense of their self-importance.

The ignorant public is incapable of understanding when barriers need to be broken down and the existing order and authority opposed and challenged — and when one needs, on the opposite, to find the authority to rely on. However, recognizing such moments in history and fully appreciating the difference requires a long-term and deep awareness of the context — i.e., simply put, one needs to expend considerable effort in order to acquire a fundamental system of knowledge and experience.

Again "we've come full circle," as they say…

I was once kindly invited to a listening session at a friend of a friend's apartment, as he recently has bought a pair of used *Apogee* "Stage" loudspeakers in Great Britain and brought them to Moscow. When I walked into the typical Soviet apartment room with no acoustic treatment, of course, I saw the loudspeakers positioned quite haphazardly in free spots between pieces of furniture and connected to some random set of electronics (also bought used over the Internet, apparently). Having sold most of the components at *Purple Legion* back in the day and knowing their properties, I can say that they were sort of OK but belonged to the "not all that glitters is gold" category.

If the host's goal was to set a record by buying this set of equipment at the lowest price possible, he might have made it into the Guinness Book of Records (even considering the fact that the speakers arrived from England with one of the tweeters apparently having some problems). Knowing the sound of those loudspeakers intimately, at my friend's place I would give the system's sonic performance a "two plus" on the five point scale at best — even while giving the host a benefit of a doubt taking into consideration the much less than perfect source and amplifying equipment and the listening environment deficiencies. Although, how could that be any different?! Despite his most likely objections that I am wrong, apparently his main goal was just to buy all this stuff at the lowest possible price. For that achievement I would readily give him "five" out of five.

The system's owner was evidently right in believing that it is senseless to dwell endlessly on theory alone, that one needs to put it into action at some point. But he was wrong in believing that one could eventually stumble upon a "golden nugget" of an audio system by simply serially experimenting with various random setups with no methodology except relying on his or her own (usually very limited in scope, I must say) outlook and the *Nullius in verba* principle.

This sort of "audio promiscuity" only has two positive outcomes: first, it should eventually teach audiophiles that time is the most precious thing we have, and, second, despite almost zero amortization of audio equipment due to its use, it should also immediately teach them to view (as a rule, quite significant) losses inherent in its replacing as a given, similar to the losses inherent in a used car's subsequent sale.

Relying only on his limited — because of the lack of knowledge and experience — intuition (I judge from my post-audition conversation with him), the host did not even work out a direction *where and why* he is moving sonically. As a result it is very unlikely that he will follow any path to its final destination, abandoning just bought items halfway through and already eyeing the next "bargain" on the various Internet "audio marts."

The host told me that because he was "stung so many times," he doesn't trust anybody's opinion and relies only on "his own ears," his goal is to explore and try a lot of equipment with least expense to finally settle on something suitable. However, I'm afraid that exploring component properties in this way, leaving their potential entirely unfulfilled and, therefore, getting the wrong impressions about the components' real sonic capabilities, he will never stop — and will never find anything "suitable" (only if one day he'll not be stopped by Russian customs' officers for import tax cheating).

What he lacks the most, in my view, in order to finally find peace, is a willingness to augment his pessimism regarding others' opinions and intentions with an optimism of collective knowledge and mutual good will. I don't think that he will be able to "reinvent the wheel" in audio, which is why the denial of authority in its pure form — essential for scientific discoveries and the movements like Enlightenment — does not work for him. What does, however, is a creative attitude towards established conceptions and procedures based on, conversely, the recognition of the appropriate authoritative knowledge and experience, which will always bring his "soul's elation" in the desired harmony with reality.

Left alone to their own devices (*sic!*) while the faith in authority has completely evaporated through new information channels, both true music lovers and sworn in audio enthusiasts ended up in a highly precarious situation. Many members of the current audiophile community have no one to blame for this loss of faith in collective mind but themselves as there is a right place and a right time for that weapon of destruction and disunity that is *Nullius in verba*. And without the tool of creation and unity that is *Credent verbo* they are left defenseless when faced with a paradigm change — and having lost the faith they have hit a dead end.

In High End Audio the key role in obtaining an outstanding sonic result is played not so much by the choice of means and techniques, but inspiration, i.e. purity of intent. I have listened to very expensive gear making empty sounds and very inexpensive equipment sounding magical. This purity of intent's gray scale spreads across the whole range between the "soul's elation" multiplied by "art requires sacrifice" to the "what is the biggest discount I can get?" demand, which fully matches the corresponding gray scale of the sonic end results.

However, formulating and deeply feeling these good intentions is impossible for one person by himself just as it is unthinkable to convert oneself to a faith having spent all life in total isolation. Attaining a unity of convictions and conceptions requires a history, a community, an authority, a spiritual force arising from a collective faith in common ideas, that mostly rely on those shared beliefs rather than on concrete proofs.

The task of any man lies in adapting one's own opinion to this context of common faith. That is how it was at the moment of High End Audio's inception. Nowadays, with the arrival of new information technologies, we are observing a reverse mechanism: attempts of all kind to bend this context to one's own will.

In terms of finding new, concrete data new information channels open up incredible opportunities. But without an algorithm of a unified creed, an isolated, self-absorbed, aspiring audiophile or music lover will inevitably get lost in the labyrinth of chaotically grabbing separate pieces from a pile that was once a picture, assembled from a puzzle. Having lost his faith, in fear of constant twists and turns of this labyrinth, a secluded audiophile will never be able to re-assemble the puzzle again.

As **David Deutsch**, a British theoretical physicists and designer of quantum computers, wrote in his book *The Beginning of Infinity*, from which I borrowed two Latin expressions for this section's title:

"In fact, progress requires the application of an ever increasing body of knowledge which predates our observations."

The fundamental reason for our fascination with music and sound is every human being's pursuit of integrity, in other words — the pursuit of happiness. Even if, as a prominent Russian audio critic **Maria Savina** (an accomplished theoretical physicist in her own right) once said, some need the musical equivalent of a "puke" to do so, and others — "some white chicks wailing by the fireplace."

Because High End Audio finds itself at the intersection of technology and art its fundamental method requires the use of *holistic* knowledge (unlike the purely utilitarian approach) meaning both of the "isolated" kind — based purely on objective information — and of the "connected" one — which can be passed only from one like-minded individual to another strictly within the context of complete mutual trust.

Such holistic knowledge allows one to clearly see one's own reflection in the "mirror" that is another person. But it is only possible when that other person is neither an emptiness nor a fun-house mirror, purposefully distorting the reflection, but a person who feels genuine compassion for you and sincerely wants to help. He does not necessarily need to be hundred percent like-mined but at the very least has to have good intentions and be prepared to speak the same language as you do.

With the help of any other art form, people can find a source and stimulus for personal growth through the formation of such mutually trusting relationships. The same applies to audio. However, without an opportunity for a "heart to heart" conversation and a strong urge to find (or learn!) a common language, no progress is ever possible.

Such mutually trusting relationships between like-minded individuals are a prerequisite for obtaining any significant results, because outside of them a large part of the total knowledge — the "connected" one — cannot be passed. Without them no wholesome inner evolution of a human being is possible — our most fundamental questions, which need the answers to facilitate the process of inner growth, will be forever left without the right answers.

The main drawback of the present moment lies in the fact that a crowd of millions across the whole world is working hard at different levels to ensure that the right questions remain unasked, God forbid — and that the wrong ones will be constantly reiterated, as long as this *perpetuum mobile* uninterruptedly pumps terabytes from one muddy pool spot of the Internet data to another (so that interested parties can endlessly "catch fish in these dark waters.") All this is done by "powers that be" out of fear that the right answers will immediately cause these pumps to jam, and will put a stop to a myriad of business deals that rely on.

It is therefore no coincidence that, as the Internet capabilities were constantly improving for this particular use — so the right questions and the right answers all but gone from the Internet radar screens of even the most dedicated audiophiles — High End Audio continued to fare worse and worse.

Meanwhile, for any true art to function well it needs support of all kinds — usually coming from the government and the social elite — that will not only support its physical existence but also create the demand for it through appropriate cultural and educational programs.

If left to their own devices purely market-based relationships cause all the members of the art community to if not gradually degrade to the level of "anti-art" but just go through the motions of delivering superficial, even if elaborate in design and production, pure craftsmanship that will be catering to predominantly primitive or indifferent public.

Against the backdrop of other factors that affected the decay of the High End industry lately — technological, socio-economic and demographic — as well as the lack of consumer audio standards, not to mention the declining desire for deep musical experience among the general population, the factor of Internet promotion in every way facilitating of anonymous exchange of information and social atomization, which both prevent the uninhibited transfer of *holistic* knowledge — only through which the whole potential of the aesthetic aspect of High End Audio can be fulfilled — served as the "baseball bat" that ultimately "broke the neck" of the industry's most established *modi operandi*.

As with any coin proverbial democracy has a flip side. The faceless and anonymous Internet communication is unquestionably good for promoting everything that can be easily digitized. As for everything else, because of buildup of the endless cycles of mistrust between the anonymous and atomized Internet dwellers, it is only capable of becoming an insurmountable obstacle to establishing any trust between them.

The chain reaction of total mistrust of each other — reinforced with the arrival of the Internet — is the most fundamental reason that led to today's "great audiophile tragedy."

Chapter 6. THE HOLY GRAIL

What does the functionality of High End Audio really mean?

A COMPLETELY BLURRED VISION

Both due to the lack of commonly accepted consumer sound quality standards in High End Audio and its other pitfalls mentioned above the industry's vision of its own main purpose and day-to-day internal processes has gradually lost the focus.

In other words, on both sides of the "sales counter barricades", there is a total confusion regarding the very nature of the products that the High End Audio industry offers, which, given today's digressive stage of its development, presents the fundamental obstacle for "passing the torch" to a new generation of audiophiles.

These potential new customers are confused mainly because a whole number of disparate products and phenomena coexist under the common umbrella term of High End Audio.

The efforts of some of its adepts seem to be aimed at studying the sensitivity of the human hearing apparatus; others seem to be under the spell of the typical insecurities of an "anal-retentive" fixation of hoarding and collecting; certain audiophiles clearly use all this equipment for nothing more than just satisfying their irrepressible need for boosting their self-esteem. While for inveterate technocrats, it does offer them a chance to be involved with some of the most cutting edge solutions and technologies, nevertheless, the dominant hoopla in High End Audio currently takes place around the numerous means of endlessly polishing "audio steam engines."

If the industry's veterans take this mess for granted one can easily imagine the confusion that all these disparate fumblings cause among the uninitiated.

I think that this confusion is the main reason for the lack of any "fresh blood" in High End Audio — as the influx of it requires clear answers to the following questions:

— How are we supposed to perceive an industry that has not yet formulated — clearly and exhaustively — the main idea that lies at the core of its existence that explains such a disparate mix of its currently produced products? (If videophiles were still buying in frenzy the old VHS videocassette recorders — hello, vinyl junkies! — the same question could has been addressed to the video industry, but they do not.)

— What does the original functionality of High End Audio really mean then? And did it stay the same since its inception?

— How necessary is it to squeeze — with the help of turntables worth $150,000, tonearms worth $25,000 and a cartridge for $15,000 — the last drops of dubious information out of $1 000 a pop "first press" vinyl records (such as, for example, the noise of an air conditioner that was on during the recording sessions at the studio)?

— Do we really need to pay those $1,000 for *first press* vinyl records or, let's say, $500 for "master" copies on magnetic tape to truly appreciate the music that is recorded on them?

— Is its ability to raise its owners' self-esteem the only reason for the existence of "audio jewelry" or are there any other solid reasons for covering parts of a tonearm with pure gold?

— How important are the latest hi-res gimmicks for hearing and digesting the most subtle musical emotions, ideas and messages?

— And finally, even if there is a myriad reasons to claim that "the future of audio is in the past," what exactly are we supposed to bring over from the past to the present — and what should be left there to rest in peace forever?

These are the questions that would inevitably arise in the head of any casual observer when watching a typical "audiophile circus" on tour.

However, sincere attempts of the most prominent audiophile media to come up with exhaustive answers to any of them are too scattered and rare (and still, as a rule, are not too conclusive) to be really visible and adequately appreciated by anyone except some seasoned hardcore types.

When I read some heated debates over particular products on the Internet audio forums one thing becomes apparent: the fundamental reason for these disagreements is not so much the very properties of the components that are being discussed but the entirely different personal needs that drove the forum members to using them in the first place.

Thus, all of the holy audio wars — analog vs. digital, home audio vs. portable and so on, not to mention arguments about which hardware is the best — are based on the conflict between representatives of various "strains" of the audiophile hobby which are totally incompatible with each other.

Heated and irreconcilable arguments arise precisely because the original reasons for the serious interest in audio among the parties involved are also incompatible.

I would not issue a verdict on which of these reasons are "better" and which are "worse" or who deserves to be considered a "true audiophile" as, in all honesty, this would be an equivalent of arguing over what is better — apples or steaks.

Nevertheless, the incredible level of open hostility on the Internet audio forums is directly related to the stress of the forced coexistence under the same "roof" of High End Audio of not just incompatible personal convictions, but almost entirely irreconcilable fundamental *ideas, goals* and *reasons* for this passion. These contradictions are then exacerbated by the zealous streak that is typical of many audiophiles' personality, seemingly as a result of an inherent desperate need to prove their self-esteem within a context of belonging to the right — in their subjective opinion — group or creed.

The intensity of arguments can be akin to placing a fundamentalist Muslim, an Orthodox Jew and a Christian in a single chat room. One would then observe the same uncompromising and active fanaticism, which in its ferocity is quite close to the one arising during a discussion among audiophiles of their preference in terms of, for example, loudspeaker cable brands.

I am convinced that if the entire audiophile community openly rationalized the real causes and mechanisms of this forced co-existence under the all-encompassing sign of High End Audio it would be able to dispense with almost all of its internal contradictions and resolve almost all of its inner conflicts by demonstrating not this much — even if it's dormant — hate towards each other but much more love. Moreover, to avoid further trouble, some of its thus consolidated crews can also embark on their own favourite "boats" — with whatever names — and to sail away in the direction of their various native promised lands for good..

Therefore, if today's incarnation of — let's call it genuine — High End Audio is relying on its future productivity, it should state its fundamental mission clearly and without beating around the bush. Otherwise, its various "strains" in an attempt to take the initiative from each other and therefore pulling its core in different directions — like the proverbial swan, crayfish and pike — will eventually tear it apart, bringing the original whole industry to its logical finale (this drastic difference of agendas of various High End Audio fractions was the actual reason why any of several attempts to set up a trade association for the industry always failed).

This turn of events is inevitable when a multitude of essentially unconnected products and phenomena are defined by a single label, using which "in vain" entirely clouds an outside perspective on the industry.

Evidently, not everyone who considers himself to be a part of this occupation (as much as they try to convince everyone, most of all themselves, to the contrary) actually needs true High End Audio. If one assumes for a minute that true High End Audio is defined in categories close to the ones that I propose below…

In my opinion, if, having lived to a respectable age, you are still listening to "music for pimple-face teenagers", and you have no plans for further developing your music appreciation skills, you do not really need a high-end system at all. And if, in addition, you don't know what to do with your money, something entirely different would be suitable to your needs: for instance, an audio system of the "Big Bang Audio"[1] variety. However, if you are prone to unending bouts of nostalgia for "*those were the days, my friend*"[2] — you likely

---

[1] I.e., a system designed for playing hard rock music very loudly.

[2] A line from "Those were the days", a song written to the tune of Boris Fomin's "By the Long Road" romance, performed by Paul McCartney's protégé, Mary Hopkin, in 1968.

require something in the vein of "Golden Age Audio"[3] set up. And so on...

Without such a *revision* of all the corresponding "strains" of various audiophile communities and their needs the motley crew of contemporary players instead of cooperating with each other (as the spirit of community should theoretically imply) and creating some sort of a consolidated offering, will continue working against each other, fruitlessly and endlessly trying to prove something to each other.

Furthermore, such interspecies aggression also completely disorients the market of new potential consumers as, on the one hand, this confrontation continues under the common flag of the proverbial High End Audio, but, on the other, juggling mutually exclusive ideas in front of neophytes is unlikely to look convincing or appealing.

In the latter case, in terms of the potential flow of "fresh blood" in true High End Audio (i.e. those curious outside observers which are the only ones who can save it from total decay in forthcoming future), the High End Utopia inevitably turns into a Dystopia.

And not because the goals and purposes of its various fractions are unattainable, but merely because these goals and purposes remain out of focus and therefore — entirely indiscernible.

So the urgent need to clearly formulate High End Audio's fundamental *raison d'être*[4], i.e. its key utilitarian purpose, or, in other words — its key functionality does exist.

Let's start from the very beginning...

---

[3] Either "vintage" audio equipment that was made in the distant past and retrieved from decades of storage, or modern equipment designed to resemble the looks and the sound character of equipment from the 1930s and the 1940s, the period known as the "golden age of audio."

[4] *French.* The most important reason or purpose for someone or something's existence.

'Everyone Listens to the Music They Listened to When They Were Fourteen Years Old...'

There is a well known saying, "everyone listens to the music they listened to when they were fourteen years old." Meaning that, in a sense, a given individual chooses his native "music language" no more that he chooses his native verbal one.

Namely, as elementary as this may sound: if one is born in a society where everyone speaks Russian, one will start speaking Russian, a society where everyone speaks English — English, Chinese — Chinese, and so on.

Moreover, these processes of native language formation are so deep that Noam Chomsky states: "...even in their crying, German infants reproduce the melodies of German speech, French infants — of the French one. This trait is seemingly acquired *inside the mother's womb*. Within the first year of their life, children master the sonic system of their mother tongue, and begin to be involved in meaningful conversations... several years later."[5]

Thus we are imbued with a native musical "language" with our mother's milk, in an entirely arbitrary and often accidental fashion at a strictly defined moment of our personal development.

One must note that after that development process is fully completed the "musical window in our heads" closes, and learning a new "musical language" essentially presents the same problem as mastering a *foreign* verbal language (i.e. requires a concentrated effort, as well as some sort of a methodology, additional technical means, etc.).

In the same work Chomsky denotes the *homo sapience*-specific ability to learn any human language as *language ability*,

[5] Noam Chomsky, Robert Berwick. *Why Only Us: Language and Evolution (translated from Russian)*.

and defines the *basic property of a language* as the following: "... language is a computational system that produces an infinite number of expressions, each having a specific interpretation within the semantic-pragmatic and the sensory-motor systems (roughly speaking, thinking and speech)."

Without going into too much detail, let us note that the devotees of sound of a particular "flavor" — whether it is tube or transistor amplifiers, electrostatic or horn speakers, vinyl turntables or digital sources and so on — very rarely change their preferences. Thus, one can justifiably speak of a native sonic language of sorts in this area of aesthetic perception as well.

> Twenty-five years ago we struggled to sell a demo pair of *Martin Logan* CLS loudspeakers for years at the original *Purple Legion* store, attributing this difficulty to the speakers' specific trait — they were capable of reproducing *only* the grand piano in a very satisfactory manner. For any other program material, despite their upper midrange and high frequency resolution, their sound was "lacking body" to a degree that it was hardly acceptable. But one day, as I came into the office I was greeted with a cheerful remark: "Can you imagine, we sold the *CLS* today!". "Who bought them?", I asked, getting the reply: "A grand piano tuner, who has never had any previous exposure to 'serious' audio".

If we would accept the aesthetic side of high performance audio as an inevitable aspect of it then sound delivery peculiarities of concrete audio equipment that have impressed an individual at a certain critical point of his or her life become their native sonic language. And transition to a different (possessing a different set of expressive capabilities which could be more appropriate to ensure steady personal growth) sonic communicative channels to connecting with music differently requires, just like learning foreign languages, considerable additional effort — moreover, a fully conscious one.

A question may naturally arise: what then is the point of learning new "musical languages" (and/or "sonic" ones, for that matter)?

The answer to that question lies in awareness of the necessity for steady spiritual growth.

Throughout thousands of years music has been one of the means for the deepest and most meaningful communication between people, and humanity's musical heritage that has been accumulated over that time has tremendous spiritual potential.

Unhindered access to this potential requires constant development of emotional intelligence. Meaningful communication in this case will only be made possible by a sufficiently advanced command of the musical language inherent in a given genre.

It is also worth mentioning that for the vast majority of the population native musical languages generally form with specific historical conditions of a fairly primitive (in terms of the direction and scale of that aim of consistent personal spiritual development with the help of music) communicative social environment.

And the probability of a fairly primitive native musical language forming in a typical listener is so high.

LEARN, LEARN AND LEARN![6]

To determine the original functionality of High End Audio equipment we need to go back to the very roots of this phenomenon.

As mentioned before, the ideology of High End Audio was initially developed by the movement's founders in the context of reproducing recordings of "serious" (usually acoustic) music, performed in a natural acoustic space. This equipment was originally intended to be used mostly by aficionados of the classical and other academic music. But what makes up the set of consumer characteristics of audio equipment of this kind — which must be altogether absent from the more "down-to-earth" equipment?

In the socio-cultural context of High End Audio's first formation years and even decades when the principal consumers of High End Audio were highly educated, successful and accomplished professionals brought up in a certain cultured environment, the explicit evaluation of its functionality was not really necessary, and any detailed discussions on the topic were superfluous.

Today due to social, economic, demographic and other changes in society, when — in order to determine the capabilities of high performance audio equipment — it is paramount to answer that question, it becomes obvious that the main functionality of High End Audio is *educational. This class of audio equipment is an instrument for learning foreign musical languages (or a constant improvement of one's proficiency in them).* Accordingly, the sound quality of the audio equipment in this class has to be assessed by the instrumental capabilities — specific for this particular application — which it demonstrates. For instance, super expensive exotic alloys for hammer heads or their handles, made of fine ebony and

---

[6] A very famous quote by Lenin, who called upon the mostly illiterate revolutionary masses to constantly educate themselves.

polished to micron tolerances, let alone, for example, gold plating of microscopes' external chassis don't really improve the instrumental capabilities essential to these particular tools. The same "separation of the grain from the (as a rule, unnecessarily expensive) chaff" should be applied when evaluating the *educational* instrumental sound quality capabilities of High End Audio equipment.

That definition of High End Audio's main functionality above is fully supported by my own personal experience. People who own audio systems of this caliber often acquire an advanced proficiency in musical languages, previously foreign to them, it carries their main interests to new musical territories — while the rest continue to listen mostly to basically the same music that they "listened to when they were fourteen years old."

When I was fourteen years old, I lived in Snezhinsk, a small town in the Ural mountains. A technical university graduate who just arrived in town to work as an engineer at the local nuclear research facility would sometimes gather friends in his ten-square-meters dorm for music listening sessions. In that room he had installed one of the most sophisticated mass-produced audio systems in the Soviet Union and would entertain his visitors with the best vinyl recordings of classical music he could get his hands on, some released by the state owned *Melodiya* label, some from other socialist countries.

One day I was invited too, and as he was seeing us off, walking along the long corridor of the dormitory, we heard the thunder of Jimi Hendrix' *Purple Haze* blasting from another room — to which our audiophile host remarked with contempt: "If Stalin were still in power, we would not be forced to hear this shit".

I cannot say that I really appreciated his comment at the time (I was fifteen then, and I cannot say that I really liked the music that he played to us either). And his words, naturally, did not prevent me from listening to Jimi Hendrix but what that first true audiophile in my life meant (and he definitely wasn't referring to the benefits of Stalin's purges, but the positive effects of the cultural policies of the early USSR, namely compulsory education and "enlightenment" of the masses) resonated deeply with the period that followed — of my obsession with the possibilities that true High End Audio gear provided me with for subsequent musical growth.

Speaking of historical specifics of applying High-End technology in practice, for the first adepts of the movement it was a case of perfecting their knowledge of musical languages they were already proficient in. As for today's audiophile generation, which for the most part has absorbed the language of primitive pop-music with "their mother's milk", it will be a much more difficult task of learning new languages of serious music from the ground up (for instance, the languages of "serious" jazz or academic classical music).

In terms of promotion, High End Audio's original nature, its colossal educational potential — is, undoubtedly, a mixed blessing. Essentially, in order not to scare potential customers away and not to imply that any additional efforts are required on the consumer's part, this industry has always tried — as paradoxical as it sounds! — to keep its main mission concealed.

As the contemporary Consumer Electronics industry is seemingly viewed by most of its players as an *entertainment* industry, its High End Audio part has also always kept its educational aspect muted, while simultaneously hyping its entertaining application (which, in its turn, seems contrived considering typical audiophile "no pain, no gain" scenarios).

THE THIRD DIMENSION

Scientific studies of all kinds have conclusively shown that the efficiency of learning a new foreign language is substantially higher given the pronounced effect of *three-dimensionality* of the sound used (whether that of a teacher's voice or specially developed "linguaphone" systems which can recreate 3D sound field through either loudspeakers, standard headphones or In-Ear Monitors (IEMs, or simply in-ear/ear monitors)).

In September of 2009 at the *CEDIA* trade show in Atlanta **Gary Reber** of the *Widescreen Review* magazine brought the *Smyth-Research* "Realizer' processor to my attention. It's based on a proprietary revolutionary technology of reproducing 3D sound through headphones and in-ear monitors. I immediately went to their show booth and despite a fairly tedious user-calibration procedure I was flabbergasted by fully palpable three-dimensionality of the sound presentation provided by some entry-level *Stax* headphones that were used for *Smyth-Research*'s multi-channel Home Theater demonstration.

When I was enthusiastically relaying my first impressions of "Realizer" to a distinguished manufacturer of headphones and vinyl cartridges, **John Grado**, stopping by at his Brooklyn factory on my way home, he asked me, perplexed: "What is all that for, especially for stereo recordings?"

John's question took me aback: indeed, the main use of the "Realizer" was supposed to be the reproduction of multi-channel music recordings and film soundtracks. Nevertheless, as a hardcore audiophile, I have always taken a virtually three-dimensional soundstage in decently reproduced music in domestic environment as a given, but because it always seemed impossible the first exposure to full recreation of the 3D spatial effect through headphones made an indelible impression on me.

Although my intuition told me that the more information one hears the better — and information from the "third dimension" has to be as in-demand with the listeners as that from the first two — I wasn't able to come up immediately with a sufficiently persuasive argument for the "Realizer's" extreme significance to John. Among other reasons, that was because my interview with **Lorr Kramer**, *Smyth-Research*'s US representative, which let me found out a number of crucial details of this project, would only take place several months after that particular visit to *Grado Labs*'s factory.

Next January I spent the whole day in Los Angeles on a marathon race through three individual calibrations for my own "Realizer", first at the historical Egyptian Theater in Hollywood and then at two studios: one for DVD mastering ("*Mi Casa Multimedia*"), the other for multichannel recording ("*AIX Studios*").

Several days prior to that I also interviewed Lorr in Las Vegas for my personal column in *Audiomagazin*.

During the interview he mentioned how the "Realizer" project began. When the company's owners sold the multi-channel sound technology for films and music — DTS — that they developed, and began to think of what to do next, they were approached with an offer to design a set of headphone-related equipment for the learning of Japanese via the Internet.

A question arises: what is the connection between learning Japanese over the Internet and 3D sound reproduced through headphones?

As Lorr explained, they soon found out that the effectiveness of learning a foreign language, especially its phonetics, is directly linked not only to the highest overall sound resolution but also to a particular aspect of the resolution — its three-dimensionality. The subsequent research and development in general-purpose three-dimensional sound reproduction through headphones significantly expanded the scope of the initial project's goals and eventually required all of the company's resources to be fully concentrated on a much broader appeal product..

While Lorr was talking about that starting phase of the "Realizer" project, memories of my own self-learning of English — with the help of listening to *BBC World Service* programs on a shortwave receiver back in the 80s — flashed through my head. The reception quality was so terrible that I had to look up every word I heard in the dictionary using a transcription by choosing among several words that sounded alike — depending on their context.

According to Lorr, even considering the decent quality of dual channel sound reproduction available via the Internet at the time, it was clearly insufficient to effectively grasp all the nuances of an unfamiliar language. Because clear perception of these also requires that "third dimension". If the first two sonic dimensions allow one to hear *what* is being said, the third one provides a better understanding of *how* it is done.

The reason that the so-called "sound stage" always got so much attention in High End Audio is directly related to the fact that the third dimension of the "stage" allows us to better hear not only *what* the musicians are playing but also *how* they are doing it.

An explanation of the significance of *Smyth-Research's* technology for comprehending the audiophile pursuit, which I could have given to John Grado when he questioned my (over) excitement regarding the "Realizer", suddenly occurred to me several years later when I was, yet again, pondering why we put so much effort, money and time into this obsession.

The main goal of all these efforts should be the recreation of this "third dimension" in stereo recordings.

This is what appropriate conditions in listening rooms have to be created for, that's why we need to use the best electronics and why we should apply sophisticated means of all kinds for tweaking our audio systems.

And this is why I see a huge potential in such sonic 3D technologies as, for instance, implemented in BACCH 3D processor by **Edgar Choueiri**, which can extract the desired third dimension even from mono recordings (which I was able to make sure of myself at a demonstration of the processor at his Manhattan apartment a few years ago).

Reproducing the convincing third dimension (or, in other words, reproducing a stunningly detailed and tightly focused virtual sonic "sound stage") is a direct manifestation of the highest resolution of an audio system. This is why the degree of the manifestation of this third dimension in sound reproduction serves, in a way, as a "litmus test" of a piece of equipment's belonging to the highest class possible — True High End Audio.

SOUND QUALITY
FROM THE HIGH END AUDIO PERSPECTIVE

The pursuit of the most realistic reproduction of music's three-dimensionality has always been considered in the sonic ideology of the forefathers of High End Audio as the search for its Holy Grail (even if one had to read between the lines to see it).

Thus, the degree of manifestation of the desired primary effect — the "holography" of sound, the lifeblood of High End Audio — is the main criterion for assessing sound quality within its context.

This conclusion necessarily serves to explain why only a subjective auditioning allows one to fully judge the sonic qualities of audio equipment.

Despite all the accumulated knowledge regarding the inner workings of our hearing apparatus when it is perceiving sound spatially, we still don't have reliable means of the perception's precise technical mapping. This is why no methods for objectively assessing stereo imaging specifics in any given case exist — any currently accepted technical measurement procedures (apart from their role in devising new standards, corresponding calibration methods and appropriate tools to meet them under specific conditions) when applied to analyze sound field spatial perception data, usually turn out to be of a very limited use. Even if there exist some technical ways to precisely analyze the spatial stereo imaging perception, which I seriously doubt, I would imagine how cumbersome those procedures can be, especially compared to the ease of subjective evaluation of the spatial effects by trained experts.

This is why, given the lack of commonly accepted sound quality standards, High End Audio's main method of subjective equipment auditioning, which serves to assess — among other criteria — the degree of "solidity" of recreated sonic images (let us remind ourselves of the very nature of "stereo" patent by Blumlein) represents the only way of getting back to the very roots of the original "stereo" technology.

Our definition of the main sound quality criterion also contains the reason why we called the design and production methods of typical mass-market equipment a shift from the primary to the secondary. It also explains why any audio products that rely primarily on conventional sets of objective technical measurements and data regarding description of their sonic qualities are second-rate by definition.

As soon as we were able to define the highest degree of sonic "holography" as the fundamental criterion for confirming the status of the most advanced stereo systems (i.e. those that truly belong to the class of High End Audio), all of my (ostensibly, disparate) previous arguments seem to immediately begin to come together in a single cohesive whole.

First, regarding the specifics of personal development process of formation of proficiency in native musical languages and the role of tightly focused three-dimensional sound reproduction in increasing efficiency of learning new ones. Second, regarding the main feature of the original "stereo" technology on which the entire foundation of High End Audio rests (reproducing "solid", that is, entirely palpable sonic images within a three-dimensional sound stage). And finally, regarding who may have any use for such a high performance audio equipment and why.

MUSICAL LANGUAGE TEMPLATES

The functioning of our brain, in order to ensure maximum efficiency, is based on creating "attractors" — *templates* of sorts.

These templates allow a musical message and its full meaning to "seep through" both one-dimensional "mono" (projecting sound along the central vertical axis) and flat two-dimensional "quasi stereo" (projecting sound along the vertical axis and the horizontal one) even though the sound quality can be just a bit more than mediocre.

This is why back in my days of sitting by the short-wave radio receiver listening to *BBC World Service* I could become ecstatic from the music that I was hearing: certain templates that I have accumulated by then were triggered in my head and could fill the perception gaps in my brain activity despite the very low quality of the radio reception.

From the above the following can be suggested: given fully formed language templates in someone's head sound quality seemingly no longer has a significant effect on the full perception of familiar genres of musical information (compare this to the full perception of what is being said even given a very poor connection over the phone).

At the same time, *for the process of forming new linguistic templates (including musical ones), through which a fluent command of corresponding languages is developed, the highest possible sound quality (the main manifestation of which is its three-dimensionality) is the most fundamental parameter that affects its efficiency.*

It is entirely possible that this increase in efficiency is correlated with the fact that, under natural conditions, our brain is used to dealing with three-dimensional sounds only, which is why it requires a direct and habitual access to the *totality* of corresponding phonetic signals in order to quickly form linguistic templates. Thank God that the "ancient" technology of stereo recording gives us that opportunity!

By way of illustrating the statement on the increased efficiency of forming new "musical templates" as a result of the highest possible sound quality, justifying the very right of High End Audio to exist, let me give you a couple examples. One of them is a direct confirmation of the thesis (although, seemingly from a different slant), the other — a brief description of my own relevant experience.

Firstly, among High End Audio equipment users I have almost never met "serious" academic musicians (who form their musical templates in conservatories) or even any of the hardcore "*melomaniacs*" (very knowledgeable music collectors, whose templates have, it seems, been stuck in their heads for quite a long time, urging them to collect records within the confines of very strictly defined genres).

Obviously there are wealthy people in both groups, they can afford to buy a truly high performance audio system for personal use. It just seems that they simply have no need for it as all the "musical templates" they need in their life have already been formed in their heads a long time ago. As for forming the new ones — it appears that they feel no need for them.

And secondly, I have seen many times how one of High End Audio's founding fathers, **Arnie Nudell**, the founder of *Infinity* and *Genesis Loudspeakers*, was always against playing "dumb" rock and pop music during his unforgettable audio demonstrations at various audio shows. These refusals implied that his truly exceptional loudspeakers were created for something entirely different (we now know for what!) which is why he always insisted on offering an exhibition's visitors a chance to dive into the enchanting sounds of classical music — usually entirely foreign to the vast majority of them.

WE ARE WHAT WE LISTEN TO

Therefore, *the true meaning of High End Audio lies in satisfying the listeners' need for mastering new musical languages, with the help of advancing which they would be able to appreciate — at increasingly deeper levels — the subtlest nuances of the greatest composers' musical thoughts, which, in turn, can be artfully interpreted by the most outstanding performers.*

... thus allowing listeners who are consciously trying to improve themselves to fulfil the colossal potential of their own spiritual growth with a help of direct connection to the most precious music.

Every passion is based on some primal need that requires the catalyst for the fascination, which in turn launches the subsequent chain of acquiring novel experiences to satisfy the craving — if appropriate conditions are created.

Once upon a time the allure of new music from the *BBC World Service* radio broadcasts, especially the music from John Peel's radio shows, served as another catalyst for my passion to grow via music, and that fascination created a very strong motivation for persistent learning of English; and without subsequently mastering this language I would never had acquired another instrument for widening my outlook and gaining invaluable experience. Without these new skills not only would my subsequent career had likely taken an entirely different track but also this book would had never seen the light of day.

Similarly, the sonic enchantment of truly high-end audio systems can be such a motivating catalyst, and then, according to their intented application, they can be used as an instrument for the constant widening of the listener's outlook and a constant satisfaction of his or her need for mastering the deepest meanings expressed in the language of the most serious music.

Forming new and powerful musical language templates cannot happen without a methodology, outside help, large amounts of practice — last but not least — a teaching audio equipment chain with the highest sonic resolution capabilities possible. (just try learning a foreign language using international phone calls!).

This is what *Smyth-Research* found out almost immediately when started their work on their Japanese language learning project. And this is why we have High End Audio.

Naturally, live performances in concert halls can play a role of such specialized "teaching equipment" (given an internal response to the corresponding sonic catalyst for the fascination with music) but considering the lack of one's opportunities to visit them on a regular basis, a high-end system can perform that function as well.

My "commoner" background notwithstanding, I noticed my musical preferences changing fundamentally as soon as I dove into High End Audio. After the years that I devoted to the learning of new musical languages with the help of audiophile systems I can say with certainty that I began to fluently speak the languages of, for instance, traditional jazz and popular classical music, initially new to me — and now these are my main languages of musical communication.

At the same time all of my childhood friends who had no pronounced interest in audio (or appropriate opportunities) are still listening to the same music they listened to when they were "fourteen years old."

DRIVING NAILS WITH MICROSCOPES

The ceaseless attempts made by some of the High End Audio industry players to sell its products as mere status symbols, or as audio versions of some voodoo magic relics are doomed to fail simply because in order to pay ridiculous amounts of money for the alleged increments of sonic improvement provided by, for instance, an optional "exotic" wood record clamp worth thousands of dollars, one needs not only a phenomenal and rarely seen (in truly sane people) imagination, but also a very fat purse (which are usually mutually exclusive).

At the same time without a clear and transparent understanding of High End Audio's main purpose, its "golden age" saw many totally confused customers, bewitched by promises of sonic nirvana ideally suited to their tastes, buying the audio equivalents of microscopes and using them to, figuratively speaking, drive in "heavy metal" nails... whereas the task would have been much more successfully accomplished with the audio system equivalents of real "hammers" (which, if needed, could be equipped with 24-carat gold heads — as they say, "any whim for your money!")

These totally disoriented customers always end up totally frustrated with all the expensive gear they have accumulated. As one of them recently told me, "If I would have a choice now, I would had never bought all these "High-End" stuff, I would had rather bought some reasonably priced Japanese or Chinese equipment (and, yes, he then immediately started to rave about the sound properties of his latest toy — a second hand inexpensive reel-to-reel consumer tape deck).

However, as they say, 'everything has its end': the general disregard of cognitive dissonance between the original key functionality of High End Audio products (a musical "microscope" for a mature individual) and their actual use (a musical "hammer" for a pimply teenager) by the industry for such a long time, remains not only a reason for the humongous amount of wasted resources (predominantly, due to their arrested musical development, on the "teenagers" part) but also a serious cause for its overall confusion regarding further development.

I recently saw the head of a widely known (in certain narrow circles) distributor company that represents many prestigious and esoteric audiophile brands from all over the world in Russia. As we were saying goodbys, he started to rave about some album he strongly recommended me to listen to.

I dutifully followed his advice and listened to it... and what can I say? I had a keen interest in such type of music when I was, OK, if not fourteen, then nineteen at most.

If High End Audio distributors themselves use their equipment for the wrong purposes (i.e. "caviar to the general"), what can we expect from mere mortals who happened to get bitten by the audiophile bug?!

A RETURN TO MINDFULNESS

The lack of mindfulness regarding reasons to be involved in High End Audio — at that, at both sides of the "sales counter barricades" — served as the cause for the gradual erosion of the basic notions on the very value system of High End Audio, which ultimately led to the splintering into fractions of all kinds, described above. At the same time gradually entering the stage of total amnesia regarding its original functionality, utilitarianism and axiology, High End Audio never managed to become something radically *different* and just ended up sitting between all its placed far apart chairs.

That same lack of mindfulness served as the primary cause of the industry's gradual commercial degradation (its annual global turnover was estimated at approaching five billion dollars at the peak of its success in 1990-ies) as well as its apparent definitive decline in recent years.

Thus, half a century after its birth, the home High End Audio industry has completed its development cycle in full (and, accordingly, entered a stage of degradation — as "nothing lasts forever"). And finally turned into a "genetically modified" counterpart of large Japanese corporations from the second half of the last century (despite initially being an antidote to the latter's irrelevance to true music connoisseurs).

In a situation of increasing demand for *mindfulness* in modern society, especially among the more advanced representatives of the latest generation, exhausted by excessive consumption, the traditional home High End Audio industry has been unable so far to provide any mindful, convincing and clear-cut responce to their demand.

Nevertheless, not all is lost, I hope…

Returning to the very roots of High End Audio ideology and pulling at the right semantic strings it is possible to get the rest of it out of the swamp, where it finds itself now. It needs to clearly, convincingly and coherently state its inherent value for a new target audience, which are actually more than approachable in terms of seeing a lot of value in using audio systems of the highest caliber as originally intended. Although that would require bringing not only the industry's products technical design aspects, but also their user interface features in line with the most up-to-date technologies and social agendas.

PART

4

Chapter 7. 'Portable' Revolution

Passing the Torch

Moving to a Portable Platform

From the technical standpoint, today is the best time in the history of the high performance audio industry in terms of the scope of its supply of equipment capable of delivering an unprecedented sound quality. The most promising technologies, especially digital ones, have come a long way, and almost any music you could wish for is available at your fingertips — moreover, the vast majority of it is in various high resolution formats — so the whole nomenclature of the hardware equipment available seems to constantly become even wider and deeper than ever before. Also the used gear market has accumulated an enormous amount of incredibly high-quality audio equipment which will remain functional for many years to come and which can now be bought for "pennies on the dollar." And any information is available on the Internet in a matter of seconds.

Nevertheless, the feeling that the traditional High End Audio as a fully functional industry is living through the most dire crisis in its history still persists.

As we know, "you can never step into the same river twice" — therefore it's impossible to imagine a set of reasons that would cause all the problems that High End Audio industry accumulated, which brought a drastic fall in its demand, to suddenly disappear and for the state of its affairs to return to the way it used to be during its best years — as if in fairy tale.

Were one to highlight the main causes of this decline, apart from cultural global shifts in the role of music in society and negative socio-economic preconditions of the recent years in the West, three of them are the most relevant to us at this point: the recent *technological developments*, the *recent demographic changes* and the *recent significant increase in the population's mobility*.

Thus, assuming that the principal functionality of traditional High End Audio's legacy will remain in demand, the task of passing the torch of good old High End Audio to the new generation of audiophiles may become highly relevant — from a commercial point of view as well.

It does not mean that demand for the traditional "home" version has to disappear entirely — not at all — but its continued decline is an almost foregone conclusion. One of the unorthodox ways in which this crisis may be overcome is to generate new audiophile demand by transferring the main content of High End Audio to a new — *portable* — platform.

This transition should not be betraying sonic ideals of the traditional home High End Audio, and it's not really about "leaving the party at its height while you're still enjoying it" (it's too late now anyway). Charles Handy describes in his *The Second Curve* book how all things have a horizontal S-shaped curve of being and that we should acknowledge when we are at the top of one and be ready to begin our next curve before going downhill. So in fact it's not about "leaving the (High End Audio) party early" but more about going to yet another one.

Twenty-five years ago during the "golden age" of High End Audio, we used landline telephones. Today we use mobile phones predominantly (with no loss in connection quality, on the contrary — with a significantly expanded list of additional capabilities). In a similar vein there seems nothing that can stop us from transferring all of the main functionality of High End Audio with all of its inherent capabilities from a home platform to a portable one (again, with no loss in quality of connection with music, but on the contrary with the constantly expanding set of various additional features).

Such a transition would also be facilitated by the fact that in a portable context the most expensive and critical component of an audio system, the listening room, is entirely excluded from the sound quality equation. That advantage of portable audio over the home one would substantially simplify an access to the highest sound quality and immediately provide significant increase in such audio systems' price-performance ratio.

Actually, to deliver great sound quality within the listening room environment is very unrewarding and extremely inefficient process considering that you waste that great sound quality radiated by the loudspeakers to every single point in the room — and mostly where you absolutely don't need it. Delivering sound radiation solely to your ear drums — the only spot where you do need it — allows portable systems based on headphones or ear monitors to reach an impressive level of sound quality with much smaller expenditures and costs (sometimes tenfold!) than with fully comparable sonically home equipment.

Furthermore, the transfer of High End Audio's full sonic capability to a much cheaper portable platform can finally allow to fulfill the accumulated and unrealized potential of the high performance audio industry for its *democratization*. And its *modus operandi* in manufacturing, which relies on small artisan companies from all over the world, can make it possible for those who feel suspicious about the current sonic *status quo* in the portable audio market, to get off the hook of almost exclusively Chinese made products — the same way as fifty years ago the emergence of the almost entirely Western garage industry of home High End Audio allowed the elite segment of the audio market all over the world to get rid of the claustrophobic fear of the total dominance of mediocre goods made by large Japanese corporations.

PORTABLE HIGH END AUDIO

There are two main reasons as to why the highest segments of the audio industry has so far failed to seize this new opportunity.

On the one hand, the current highest tier portable audio segment still remains predominantly at the *"mid-fi"* stage of its development. Applying this moniker, coined by the community of seasoned home audiophiles, so broadly means that — in the context of their sonic aspirations, promotional methods and, ultimately, in terms of the equipment's sound quality — the vast majority of current dedicated portable audio products belong to a middle ground between what's taken for granted in the highest segments of mass-market home audio and what is considered more or less acceptable in relation to the products approaching the sonic performance of entry level home High End Audio.

The last statement is especially true regarding the sound quality of the vast majority of even the best portable audio acoustical transducers, i.e. the devices converting one type of energy (the electrical) into another (the acoustical), that is, all types of headphones and earphones. If some examples of portable electronics (including Digital-to-Analog Converters, dedicated headphone amplifiers, etc.), especially of desktop variety, can be very advanced and approach very closely the level of the highest audiophile aspirations, quality of execution and, ultimately, sonic performance of the best home audio equipment, then the same design and performance parameters of currently the best portable audio acoustical transducers (headphones and earphones) are usually significantly below the parameters of the best home audio acoustical transducers (the loudspeakers), especially in the context of the quest for the Holy Grail of High End Audio — the sound stage holography. This is why the mid-fi moniker is the most applicable not so much for the whole range of currently the best portable audio products per se (including used in the context of desktop audio systems) but definitely for the main body of even the most aspiring current portable audio transducers.

The vast majority of the highest tier portable audio manufacturers and their sales representatives (quite often including the promotional media "links" in the chain from the manufacturers to the consumers) typically lack truly High End Audio background. They usually jump straight to the highest segments of the industry from their positions in the world of mass-market consumer electronics or professional musical equipment. And as they generally do not have sufficient exposure to the (holographical!) sound of the most remarkable High End Audio home systems, let alone corresponding active experience, the sound quality of their products continuously stays within the range of their ingrained ("flat" — sic!) sonic notions and as such it can't really rise above the mid-fi sonic performance level they are accustomed to deal with. This is why when they demonstrate such limited sound quality aspirations and the absence of any apparent attempts to progress any further, a solid possibility can be that they just don't really think that something is amiss sonically in their products so they see no reason for any significant changes in them. And even giving the benefit of the doubt to their companies' very best intentions towards their customers' sonic endeavors, here comes a chicken and egg scenario of supply vs demand in action: if the highest tier manufacturers of the best portable audio equipment themselves don't know any better sonically, how then their customers will?!

Despite some attempts by large mass-market CE corporations to come up with very expensive "absolute" products (e.g. HE-1 electrostatic headphone system by *Sennheiser* for $55 000) their sound quality is also limited by the companies' lack of openly admitted devotion to the High End Audio's cause, which means that such products can be considered only within if not mass-market, then, at the very best, the mid-fi context. Therefore, there is no way that these products' overall sonic achievements, even if their performance does sometimes rise above the level of the most refined examples of much cheaper offerings, will be significant enough to catapult them beyond the restrains of the multiple mid-fi gravitation forces of technological, ideological, economic, marketing, political, and some other nature and to land them in the domain of truly High End Audio devices. Thus, despite their very heavy price tags, such products — due to their very provenance from large mass-market corporations, that (almost) "never put their money where their mouth is" regarding their genuine long-term adherence to the High End Audio's true system of values — as a rule, still belong to the mid-fi class.

On the other hand, the reason why most aspiring portable audio equipment has been currently stopped in its sonic development in the mid-fi stage lies in the incredible inertia of the participants of the other relevant segment of the audio industry — the old-school home High End Audio. Even adhering to the proper ideology and possessing all the necessary technical knowledge and appropriate skills, as well as more than sufficient manufacturing capabilities, they continuously refuse to accept the (urgent!) need to "tune to a new frequency" of another wave of High End Audio demand.

But now — just like half a century ago when a handful of visionaries, the number of which could be counted on the fingers of if not one hand then definitely two (J. Gordon Holt, Harry Pearson, William Johnson, Mark Levinson, Jim Whiney, Dan D'Agostino, et al) — as their response to the sonic stagnation — if not degradation — within the established hi-fi trade of the time created the whole new industry of home High End Audio from scratch in a matter of a few years, we are on the brink of a historical moment as the most progressively thinking designers and engineers will finally be able to pass the torch of true sonic values of home High End Audio to a new generation of "portable" audiophiles.

... While simultaneously creating, as their forerunners did fifty years ago, a new thriving industry — *Portable High End Audio*.

StereoPravda

To illustrate this unorthodox approach to portable audio of the highest caliber I can use the example of the developments that are currently being pursued by our company, *StereoPravda*. The main mission of *StereoPravda* is that very passing of the torch of home High End Audio to the new generation of audiophiles.

Using that expression we do mean that the sound quality of our portable systems very closely approaches the main sonic properties which we have grown accustomed to in home High End Audio systems of the highest caliber throughout all these years. With a maximal similarity in character of their sonic spatial presentation.

We are not embarrassed at all to openly state the main purpose of our products: they are made for everyone who strives, through the learning of new musical languages, to explore time and time again, one after the other, new musical territories.

We achieve this by implementing only those technical means which fully correspond to the similar proved solutions routinely used in home audio of the highest aspirations.

This chapter not only illustrates such a congruence with examples of particular design features of our ear monitors (IEMs) in the *StereoPravda* SPearphone series but also shows in great detail what separates such a high-end approach from the conventional corresponding mid-fi technologies that dominate even the highest tier of the portable audio market.

I will explain the specific reasons why we use (in-) ear monitor technology — and not a headphone technology — to reach our ultimate sonic goal — to provide the best possible sound quality in portable audio — in more details below. It's suffice to say now that no conventional headphone technology would allow our designs to arrive at such a full correspondence between the twelve Home High Audio Axioms and the twelve *StereoPravda* SPearphone Axioms (which describe the most basic listening environment set up principles, specific acoustical transducers to the ear drum coupling methods and the equipment's most basic design solutions for the two main modes of listening to music — via proper home audio system versus via proper portable ear monitor system) as our proprietary ear monitor technology based on Balanced Armature multi-driver arrays does.

Several drivers are used for the same purposes as in home audio: mainly, to split the total signal energy to separate devices so each one has to deal with only a fraction of it. The same way as all the best home audio loudspeakers are multi-driver acoustic systems all the best ear monitors are also usually multi-driver ones.

That's why because multi-driver ear monitors — or multi-driver earphones — represent the best portable audio transducer technology all our ear monitor concrete applications' descriptions below are applied to this type of devices.

THE TWELVE AXIOMS OF HOME HIGH END AUDIO

It is universally accepted by old-school audiophiles that if access to a properly treated room and the best audio equipment serve as a sufficient condition for achieving a sound of the highest quality in a household environment then the necessary condition is complying with the following (sometimes trivial) set of *Axioms of Home High End Audio* [SEE FIGURE 1].

12 AXIOMS OF HOME HIGH END AUDIO

HOME HIGH END AUDIO AXIOM #1

The key loudspeaker drivers and the listener's ears have to be located *in the same room.*	*THIS IS UNIVERSALLY ACCEPTED AMONG HOME AUDIOPHILES*

HOME HIGH END AUDIO AXIOM #2

There should be no *obstacles* between the listener and the key loudspeakers' drivers (for instance, any extended acoustic waveguides or heavy curtains).	*THIS IS ALMOST* UNIVERSALLY ACCEPTED AMONG HOME AUDIOPHILES* *"Almost" because horns and other external acoustic loading speaker components are sometimes used as waveguides, which, in my opinion, should *disqualify* such solutions from representing the true High End Audio. Even if, as some audiophiles contend, the reverse is true and such loudspeakers represent the "pinnacle of audio art" — the length of the obstacles used in them is usually fairly small compared to the distance to the listener's ears.

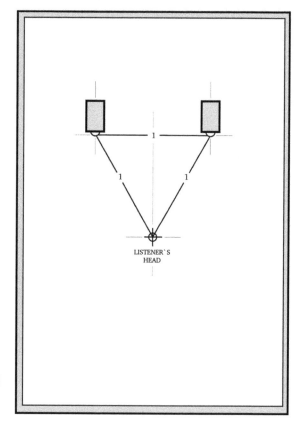

FRONTAL WALL

SIDE WALL

SIDE WALL

1

1   1

LISTENER`S
HEAD

[1]

HOME HIGH END AUDIO AXIOM #3

The listeners should be able to see — unobstructed — the key loudspeaker drivers directly *in front of them*.

THIS IS UNIVERSALLY ACCEPTED AMONG HOME AUDIOPHILES

HOME HIGH END AUDIO AXIOM #4

All the key loudspeaker drivers radiation axes have to be *parallel to each other*.

THIS IS UNIVERSALLY ACCEPTED AMONG HOME AUDIOPHILES.

HOME HIGH END AUDIO AXIOM #5

The main loudspeakers and, if applicable, their auxiliary driver units that usually operate in the lowest bass frequency band have to be *optimally* positioned relative to the physical configuration of the listening room.

THIS IS UNIVERSALLY ACCEPTED AMONG HOME AUDIOPHILES

HOME HIGH END AUDIO AXIOM #6

The left and right loudspeakers have to be *equidistant* from the listener.

THIS IS UNIVERSALLY ACCEPTED AMONG HOME AUDIOPHILES

The listener has to be located within the *near field* of the key loudspeaker drivers' acoustic radiation.

It means that within the listening room the listener has to be placed at a point where the sound intensity of the direct radiation field from the key loudspeaker drivers significantly *dominates* sound intensity not only of the acoustic field of the room's response, but the intensity of the external noise field (including, for example, the field of the loud music that leaks from the neighbors through the wall).

THIS IS UNIVERSALLY ACCEPTED AMONG HOME AUDIOPHILES

HOME HIGH END AUDIO AXIOM #8

The listener's ears have to be positioned almost *on-axis* with the loudspeakers' key drivers.

THIS IS UNIVERSALLY ACCEPTED AMONG HOME AUDIOPHILES

HOME HIGH END AUDIO AXIOM #9

The listener's ears should remain *open* throughout the duration of the listening session, and the sound stage produced by the audio system has to be perceived by the listener as located *outside* of his head, directly in front of him or her*.

* In reality when I was auditioning quite a few audio systems this is easier said than done.

THIS IS UNIVERSALLY ACCEPTED AMONG HOME AUDIOPHILES

HOME HIGH END AUDIO AXIOM #10

At the point where the listener's ears are located both a *minimal* amount of distortions and noise and the *optimal* frequency response and *flat* phase response characteristics of the audio system have to unequivocally facilitate the production of sound of the highest quality*.

THIS IS UNIVERSALLY ACCEPTED AMONG HOME AUDIOPHILES

* Which is why a considerable effort is made for *"multi-way"* electrical crossover filter networks of the highest quality to achieve the most optimal amplitude to frequency response and timing coherence of the acoustic signal from all the individual drivers in the best multi-driver loudspeakers.

HOME HIGH END AUDIO AXIOM #11

All the very best audio systems usually belong to the *active multi-way* type, i.e. they are powered by several individual amplifiers with each operating in an assigned frequency band and are set up with a help of an external active crossover unit which provides a suit of various system adjustments*.

I HUMBLY HOPE THAT THIS IS UNIVERSALLY ACCEPTED AMONG HOME AUDIOPHILES

* As opposed to *passive multi-way* single amplifier systems in which crossover filters are made of passive electronic components only.

Besides the general considerations of quality of the design and execution of the commercially available stereo equipment the quality of all "active" and "passive" electronic and mechanical parts and components inside of them — as well as the quality of its various assembly procedures — has to be *as high as possible* as it is directly correlated with the resulting sound quality.

In particular the design and execution of connecting cables — the most talked about class of separate components in High End Audio — in "no-holds-barred" audio systems is supposed to be driven exclusively by the sound quality considerations, and is not restrained by considerations of any of their mechanical properties, including durability (as a result, they can be as thick as a garden hose).*

THIS IS UNIVERSALLY ACCEPTED AMONG HOME AUDIOPHILES

* It seems that no price of any separate components, cables included, can really astound seasoned home audiophiles anymore.

The same can be said for the design and execution of home audio best cables' connectors which, within the framework of existing standards, do not imply any significant limitations on particular solutions with considerations of their physical dimensions or the wear and tear from everyday use (or even with considerations of their costs).

CHAPTER 7

Naturally, the above chart of the most fundamental overall set up *Home High End Audio Axioms* is a simplification to some extent and can be somewhat modified in one way or another, but all these minor changes are not critical for the narrative below.

TWELVE MID-FI AXIOMS FOR TYPICAL IEMS/CIEMS

Before we examine our proprietary *StereoPravda* SPearphone most fundamental principles for listening environment's set up and the most important design techniques, I suggest we look now at how both the most fundamental listening environment set up principles and the most typical design techniques are implemented in typical mid-fi ear monitors (universal tip IEMs or custom ear mold CIEMs). Despite radically different environment of sealed ear canal compared to home listening environment (with the former's Trapped Volume Insertion Gain, the occlusion effect, the bone conduction effect and a very high likelihood of premature turning on of the middle ear's stapedius reflex which inevitably leads to the hearing's temporal threshold shifts — see the pioneering research of **Stephen Ambrose** of *Asius Technologies* who published some important studies on these phenomena) we'll still do this with a purpose to see how these typical multi-driver mid-fi earphone solutions correspond to the whole list of the *Home High End Audio Axioms* above.

And then we will do the same comparison for the StereoPravda SPearphone IEMs so we can see the apparent difference between the conventional mid-fi earphones solutions and our proprietary design — and to draw some important conclusions.

To accomplish this we will use some common-sense analogies and conditional *earphone sound reproduction topology's* lingo, where [SEE FIGURES 2 AND 3]:

- earphone sound reproduction topology's virtual *living room* — the body of the IEMs/CIEMs;

- earphone sound reproduction topology's virtual *loudspeakers* — the total specific driver sections/arrays configuration, the totality of their specific individual acoustic and electrical load configurations, positioned within the IEMs' or CIEMs' body, and the dedicated electrical crossover filter networks, positioned within or outside of the earphones' bodies;

- earphone sound reproduction topology's virtual *listening room* — the operational volume of ear canals, i.e. the space that is bound by the ear canal's acoustic isolation surface[1], the eardrum surface and the surface of the ear canal walls between them;

- earphone sound reproduction topology's virtual *listener* — the listener's hearing apparatus with the eardrums by way of his or her ears.

Mapping these onto an analogous chart, we will be able to reach a number of helpful conclusions about the conditions, in which the process of listening to music usually takes place while using the typical mid-fi IEMs or CIEMs.

Without further ado...

---

[1] Determined by inner isolating curve between the surface of the individual ear mold material or the surface of a universal tip and the ear canal walls.

12 'MID-FI' AXIOMS FOR TYPICAL IEMs/CIEMs

TYPICAL "MID-FI" IEMs/CIEMs AXIOM #1

All key IEMs or CIEMs drivers (of the *loudspeakers*) are usually located *outside* of the outer contours of the operational volume of the ear canal [SEE FIGURE 2].

In other words, in case of typical mid-fi IEMs or CIEMs all of their key speaker drivers are usually located *outside* of the *listening room*.

THIS DOES NOT COMPLY WITH THE HOME HIGH END AUDIO AXIOM #1

TYPICAL "MID-FI" IEMs/CIEMs AXIOM #2

Between the *listener* and the key IEMs' or CIEMs' drivers (of the *loudspeakers*), on the sound propagation path, extended *obstacles* exist in the shape of waveguides — long and narrow sound tubes (or "sound bores" — long and winding bore holes drilled into mold material of CIEMs), which lead to the operational volume of ear canals (*the listening room*).

Additional obstacles of a different kind, *barrier acoustic filters*, are usually also located somewhere along the sound propagation path.

THIS DOES NOT COMPLY WITH THE HOME HIGH END AUDIO AXIOM #2

Due to the presence of long and/or curved waveguides/sound tubes/ sound bores, the eardrum (*listener*) never "*sees*" the (unobstructed) key IEMs' or CIEMs' drivers (of the *loudspeakers*) directly *in front of* "*him*" or "*her*" [SEE FIGURE 3].

THIS DOES NOT COMPLY WITH THE HOME HIGH END AUDIO AXIOM #3

TYPICAL "MID-FI" IEMs/CIEMs AXIOM #4

In case of typical multi-driver ear monitors, the radiation axes of IEMs' or CIEMs' drivers (of the *loudspeakers*) are usually not parallel.

It's similar to the situation when in a home loudspeaker the "tweeter" would "shoot" upwards, the midrange driver would "sing" to the side and the woofer would "pump up the bass" backwards. This is what usually seems to happen in typical multi-driver mid-fi IEMs or CIEMs during their operation.

THIS DOES NOT COMPLY WITH THE HOME HIGH END AUDIO AXIOM #4

[see the example in FIGURE 4 where the radiation of the "tweeter" driver in the right-hand bottom corner is "u-turned" by almost 180 degrees by a sound tube before heading towards the eardrum; while the other earphone's drivers are also "shooting" all over the place*.

* When the designer of these particular ear monitors confronted me at one of the recent *CanJam* dedicated portable audio shows in the US with objections that such a solution wouldn't make a sonic difference compared to the sound of the driver shooting in the sound tube "on-axis" with the tympanic membrane, his only rationale was that the sound, even in such a crooked (sic!) configuration of the wave guide, "…still has no place to propagate except along the tube." He was absolutely right, the sound had no place to go except along the sound tube walls but, at that, the sound *quality* goes down the drain.]

TYPICAL "MID-FI' IEMs/CIEMs AXIOM #5

In typical multi-driver ear monitors the operational volume of ear canals (*listening room*) is used "*as it is*", and the issue of its acoustic treatment in some way or another is irrelevant — as virtually impossible.

But what is far worse, the physical configuration of the ear monitor drivers' positions (and the corresponding waveguides/sound tubes' configuration) — usually located outside of the operational volume of an ear canal — is, in the vast majority of cases, in no way correlated to the configuration of that operational volume and is configured (or drilled) arbitrarily: depending either on the given IEMs'overall design [SEE FIGURE 2], or the particular physical configuration of an individual (custom) ear canal mold [SEE FIGURE 4].

THIS DOES NOT COMPLY WITH THE HOME HIGH END AUDIO AXIOM #5

[2]

[3]

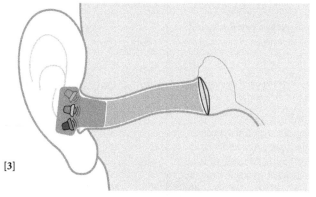

[4]

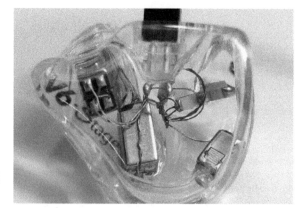

TYPICAL "MID-FI" IEMs/CIEMs AXIOM #6

In the correct positioning of a pair of ear monitors, the left and right eardrums (*listener's two* ears) automatically end up *equidistant* from the corresponding IEMs' drivers (of the *loudspeakers*) in both ear canals*.

THIS DOES COMPLY WITH THE HOME HIGH END AUDIO AXIOM #6

* A sigh of relief …

TYPICAL "MID-FI" IEMs/CIEMs AXIOM #7

The *near field* listening is defined in home audio as listening in the sound field in which the direct sound's intensity from the speakers, propagating through the air and reaching the listener's ears with no obstacles, significantly overwhelms the sound intensity of not only room-induced distortions (wall reflections, room resonances and others), but also all the noise coming from the outside (including adjacent rooms).

In case of typical mid-fi ear monitors indirect reflections arise, first as the sound is propagating through the especially curved sound tubes/sound bores inside the IEMs/CIEMs' body and then similar distortions are added during the propagation of acoustic radiation within the environment of the operational volume of the ear canal — so that the smaller the operational volume is, the better.

THIS DOES NOT COMPLY WITH THE HOME HIGH END AUDIO AXIOM #7

The ear canal's "occlusion" effect, inherent to application of any "isolating" earphones, is magnified in the case of typical mid-fi IEMs/CIEMS because they usually isolate an ear canal at the most inappropriate position — at its very entrance. Besides significantly amplifying bass frequencies by the very fact of sealing the ear canal, such shallow ear monitors' positioning increases its operational volume from that confined mostly inside the ear canal's bone part (at earphones' deep insertion) to extending to the ear canal cartilage part (at earphones' shallow insertion), which leads to the rise of the sound leakage through cartilage part's much softer (than bone part's) walls. And this is one of the main causes for the elevated "occlusion" effect. The other is lower resonant frequencies profile due to a bigger volume of trapped air at shallow insertion.

This does not comply with the Home High End Audio Axiom #7

Also the typical mid-fi IEMs/ CIEMs' ubiquitous shallow insertion principle that's universally applied due to that industry's top priority of comfort over any other priorities, sound quality included, amplifies the sonic effect of sound's "bone conduction" — that is when sound is conducted to the middle ear — in addition to the regular airborne conduction via tympanic membranes — via all sorts of facial bones, tissues and liquids.

The effect of the superposition on our auditory system will be similar to the annoyance caused by your neighbors watching the same TV channel as you in your quiet settings with their TV's volume cranked out to the very maximum.

To reiterate, in addition to the direct airborne sound radiation to our hearing apparatus (*listener*) there is the indirect significant source of it, the signal which is also coming to the middle ear through the mechanism of auditory "bone conduction." This situation is significantly exacerbated by shallow earphones' insertion and isolation, which substantially boosts (i.e. distorts) bass frequencies due to the elevated "occlusion" effect when you isolate the ear canal near its entrance. Besides detrimental sonic perception impact of premature turning on of the stapedius reflex, these two completely irrelevant for home audio effects — ear canal "occlusion" and sound "bone conduction" — cause so much interference with the direct airborne sound radiation from the earphone drivers via tympanic membrane to the middle ear that such earphones' sound presentation becomes apparently fully incompatible with a concept of "near field" listening per se. Which is the exact case of the vast majority of typical mid-fi IEMs/CIEMs*.

THIS DOES NOT COMPLY WITH THE HOME HIGH END AUDIO AXIOM #7

* Although when the key drivers of ear monitors are located *outside* of the operational volume of the ear canal (*listening room*) one cannot, by definition, speak of listening in the "near field" anyway.

Eardrums (*listener*) are *not positioned on the same axis* as the sound radiation axes of the key drivers (of the *loudspeakers*) [SEE FIGURES 3 AND 4]. The same holds true for the main vector of sound propagation within the ear canal: most driver radiation axes in typical mid-fi IEMs/CIEMs deviate significantly from it [SEE FIGURE 4], often at considerable angles.

THIS DOES NOT COMPLY WITH THE HOME HIGH END AUDIO AXIOM #8

TYPICAL "MID-FI" IEMs/CIEMs AXIOM #9

The listener's ears are usually tightly sealed when listening to the earphones and as a result of the location of the acoustic isolation line for typical mid-fi IEMs/CIEMs (as a rule, near the entrance to the ear canal) this makes the "occlusion" and "bone conduction" effects even more pronounced. The common complains that the sound images seem to be located not outside of the head, as is the case with home listening, but deeply inside, have various explanations*.

But one of them is obvious: the source of fairly significant in intensity "bone conduction" — the operational volume of ear canal — *is* located inside the head, and due to its *low-fi* quality its perceived positioning is not as easily manipulated to relieve the "inside-the-head imaging" as some dedicated DSP processing coupled with a head tracker can do to the relatively high quality airborne direct radiation from the earphones — which, of course, radiate the direct airborne signal also being positioned inside the head.

THIS DOES NOT COMPLY WITH THE HOME HIGH END AUDIO AXIOM #9

In the ubiquitous absence of adequate head-tracking implementations the "occlusion" and the "bone conduction" effects further exacerbate the fundamental problems of headphones and earphones — their "inside the head" presentation (and even if the virtual sound images perceived inside the head can be very solid and tight).

The shallow insertion of typical mid-fi IEMs/CIEMs, coupled with other serious deficiencies of their design and execution, some of which are listed here, position their perceived sound stage *deep inside the head,* with no sonic images to escape, even barely, outside of it.

* Given the typical lack of adequate quality DSP-processing working in tandem with head trackers with sufficiently high spatial and temporal resolutions, this point refers to the character of sound presentation of the vast majority of currently made headphones and ear monitors (especially, tightly acoustically isolating from the outside noise). There are just a few of most advanced suchlike DSP systems which are capable of real 3-D imaging far outside of the listener's head. They are based on special individual calibrations, transducer calibrations and constant monitoring of the listener's head movements with a fast and spatially precise head tracker. The head tracker data is fed in real time to a dedicated DSP processor which outputs stereo or 3-D multi-channel processed signal to the headphones or earphones. The best technologies of this kind allow to precisely project spatially (as it was intended by the recordings' producers) the virtual sonic images which are perceived as not positioned just "outside the head" but at substantial distances from it.

THIS DOES NOT COMPLY WITH
THE HOME HIGH END AUDIO
AXIOM #9

As a result of using primitive and low-quality "passive" crossover filters implemented with cheap parts, sonic capabilities of which are additionally limited by miniature physical size requirements, in case of typical multi-driver multi-way mid-fi ear monitor designs, significant phase shifts are created, and when they are coupled with typically suboptimal amplitude-frequency responses of such products, this results in a significant loss of resolution and micro-dynamic qualities of the reproduced music signal.

Due to the minimum size requirements for typical ear monitors', the sonic performance of mid-fi IEMs/CIEMs' "passive" electrical crossover filter networks, which divide the whole signal spectrum into several frequency bands where each one is served by a dedicated driver array, is usually significantly *worse* compared to "passive" crossover filter networks in home systems, which are not limited by their physical size and can be made with much better (and much bigger) "passive" electronic parts.

Also the manufacturers of typical mid-fi ear monitors rather than trying to fully resolve the problems of low-quality "passive" crossover filter networks and driver resonances, routinely prefer to simply "sweep them under the rug" by covering them up — as if with a "band aid" strip — with crude wide-band barrier acoustic filters installed on the way of sound wave propagation either directly on the driver's output hole

THIS DOES NOT COMPLY WITH THE HOME HIGH END AUDIO AXIOM #10

or somewhere inside the sound tubes/sound bores — which would be the same as to use a dense curtain in front of a loudspeaker to correct some of deficiencies in its sonic performance — no manufacturer would get away with such a solution in home audio, but in typical mid-fi IEMs/CIEMs industry they always do.

TYPICAL "MID-FI" IEms/CIEMs AXIOM #11

As of now — apart from our fully differential *StereoPravda* DACCA two-way DAC/tone control/crossover/amplifier and the special dedicated version of our *StereoPravda* SPearphone SB-7 ear monitors, designated as "SB-7A" — I am not aware of any commercially available portable *"active"* multi-way IEMs/CIEMs systems which would employ an external electronic crossover equipped with a sufficient set of available adjustments and a set of two separate "in-band" fully differential amplifiers.

THIS DOES NOT COMPLY WITH THE HOME HIGH END AUDIO AXIOM #11

As "active" multi-way earphone operation allows to resolve to a great extent the majority of problems inherent in using "passive" electrical filter crossover networks; accordingly, home High End Audio industry not only recognizes the fact that most of the top tier audio loudspeakers demonstrate their full capabilities only in the "active" mode but also manufactures many commercially available models of "no holds barred" absolute sound quality "active" loudspeaker systems.

While all existing multi-way typical mid-fi ear monitors, even those of the highest quality, continue to use inherently *lower-quality "passive"* filtering networks — as well as barrier acoustic filters on top of them — so the absence of open recognition of the "active" earphone operation sonic advantages over the "passive" one by the current crop of typical mid-fi IEMs/CIEMs manufacturers suggests to me that they have no immediate plans for the implementation of the most advanced approach in their products.

THIS DOES NOT COMPLY WITH THE HOME HIGH END AUDIO AXIOM #11

TYPICAL "MID-FI" IEMs/CIEMs AXIOM #12

The quality of all the "passive" materials, parts and components of typical IEMs/CIEMs (electronic, mechanical, and others) is obviously limited by their intended portable use, which is why it is usually — given the need to operate within their extremely limited physical size — fairly *low*.

This is exacerbated by the fact that, unlike home High End Audio, the mid-fi IEMs/CIEMs industry as a whole never paid too much attention to the quality of passive components.

One only needs to look at the connecting cables of typical mid-fi ear monitors to get the distinct impression that they are employed solely for their mechanical properties (of user's ultimate comfort), durability and, most likely, the lowest cost, but not at all based on the key priority — the primacy of sound quality over all other aspects of these "passive" components in the overall design.

The same, apparently, goes for the quality of various audio connectors usually used in typical mid-fi IEMs/CIEMs.

THIS DOES NOT COMPLY WITH THE HOME HIGH END AUDIO AXIOM #12

It's evident from the chart above that the fully established set of axioms defining the technological context of listening to music through typical mid-fi ear monitors (*Typical "Mid-Fi" IEMs/CIEMs Axioms*), directly reflected in the industry's ingrained approaches to their design, manufacturing, methods of coupling to our hearing mechanisms, principles for installation in the listener's ear canal and finally — last but not least — to promotion and sales, fully correspond to only one (#6) of the twelve *Home High End Audio Axioms*.

However, the main point of the charts above is to emphasize that common sense of home audio axioms, that are universally taken for granted in audiophile circles, to a large extent is based not only on elementary physics courses but also on a strict adherence to the original stereo format standard's main objective — creation of solid sonic images in a three-dimensional sound stage — which was adopted many years ago but seems to be well forgotten by now. It also rests on the totality of historical home audiophile experience, which has conclusively proven that only a *complete* adherence to the whole set of *Home High End Audio Axioms* creates the conditions essential for achieving the highest quality of *stereo* music reproduction.

THE BEHIND-THE-CURTAINS 'KITCHEN' OF PORTABLE MID-FI AUDIO

Every seasoned traditional "home" audiophile has had ample opportunity to make sure that any deviation from the strict adherence to even some of the *Home High End Audio Axioms* inevitably leads to the significant losses of sound quality.

Because there exists such an almost total discrepancy between the set of *Typical "Mid-Fi" IEMs/CIEMs Axioms* and the set of *Home High End Audio Axioms*, the main sound quality aspects of the former clearly would differ significantly from these of the latter.

Using the cause-and-effect relations in home audio as a proven foundation, you can't help seeing that these discrepancies in the case of typical mid-fi IEMs/CIEMs that are inevitable result of implementing the most established approaches to their design, execution and principles of installation within the ear canal and can only result in their evidently inferior sound quality — that is, when it's directly compared to home audio systems fully complying with corresponding *Home High End Audio Axioms*.

Experienced "home" audiophiles unlike their 'portable' colleagues are, at the very least, aware of the need to comply with all the axioms for the attainment of the highest sonic quality which — let me repeat myself — is only possible when all of the *Home High End Audio Axioms* are followed to the letter.

Even if we leave the question of the sonic qualities of modern portable electronics aside, it becomes obvious why the sound quality of portable audio systems equipped with typical mid-fi IEMs/CIEMs (born with such a flawed pedigree) has never impressed adepts of old-school home audio — considering the fact that acoustic transducers play the most significant role in establishing the sound quality of any audio system, it's not surprising at all.

Actually, the sound quality of the portable systems equipped with typical mid-fi ear monitors has to remind them a sound they would get if they are listening to a proper audiophile system properly installed in their properly acoustically treated living room, however... not from the optimal "sweet spot" within it, positioned equidistantly from the loudspeakers... but from the house kitchen (!), separated from the living room with a thick curtain and a long, narrow and winding corridor [SEE FIGURES 3 AND 5].

This sonic analogy allows us to imagine the character of the echo sound quality that will inevitably be produced in such a mid-fi *"kitchen"* — i.e. in a typical operational volume of a typical mid-fi ear monitor.

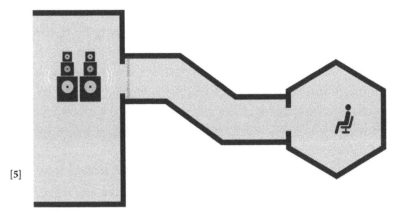

[5]

We can use the analogy because of the full similarity in the listening conditions between listening to the echo sound coming from the real listening room to the real kitchen and the listening conditions while listening to the sound from typical mid-fi ear monitors, where, in the latter case: the total driver configuration with corresponding acoustic loads and crossover filtering (*loudspeakers*) radiates sound inside their body (*living room*) and, to be heard in the ear canal's operational volume (*i.e. the "kitchen" as a listening room*) by the tympanic membranes (*listener*), the sound waves still need to propagate through the "thick curtain" covering the *"living room"* entrance (an analogy for the barrier acoustic filters routinely used in almost all commercially available multi-driver mid-fi ear monitors), then the whole length and twists and turns of sound tubes/sound bores of universal IEMs or custom CIEMs, as well as the twists and turns of the ear canal's operational volume (sufficiently extended at shallow insertion of the earphones).

To reiterate, this analogy should allow us to imagine the difference in terms of sound quality between the sonic character in the "sweet spot" of a properly acoustically treated real living room with a good stereo system installed fully following all the *Home High End Audio Axioms* and the sonic character of the mid-fi ear monitors' echo sound heard by the portable audio listener in the earphone sound reproduction topology's virtual *"kitchen"* of the operational volume in his or her ear canals using ear monitors built and installed within their ear canals in full accordance with *Typical "Mid-Fi" IEMs/CIEMs Axioms.*

This is why — due to the very close similarity of these listening conditions — the character of the echo sound from the real living room's audio playback which heard in real kitchen will be fully congruent with the sonic character heard by the portable audio listener (i.e. the real listener's tympanic membranes as the earphone sound reproduction topology's virtual *listener*) in the operational volume of his or her ear canal (the earphone sound reproduction topology's virtual *"kitchen"*) where the earphones reproduce the sound coming from the earphone sound reproduction topology's virtual *loudspeakers* set up inside the earphone bodies (the earphone sound reproduction topology's virtual *"living room"*).

Then how "high" can really be the quality of echo sound coming from the typical mid-fi IEMs/CIEMs sound reproduction topology's virtual *"living room"* into the earphone sound reproduction topology's virtual *"kitchen"*?!

And most importantly, wouldn't every attempt to improve the quality of the echo sound coming from that *"living room"* to that *"kitchen"* — by upgrading amplifiers, source components, cables, not to mention all the other auxiliary equipment and even the quality of the *loudspeakers* themselves in that *"living room"* — become no more than senseless attempts to "shoot sparrows with cannons"?! Both of these questions are rhetorical...

Therefore, to pass the torch of old home High End Audio' sonic values to the new generation of portable audiophiles, we have no other choice but to resort to unorthodox IEMs/CIEMs methods — and with the help of the unique design of our *StereoPravda* SPearphone ear monitors, special techniques of their positioning inside the ear canal and a certain method of their acoustic isolation — to try, in a way, to "teleport" — as unharmed as possible — the sound quality from the "sweet spot" of the best home High End Audio systems properly set up in properly acoustically treated real living rooms, first, to our IEMs' audio systems installed within our ear monitors' bodies and then to our customers' tympanic membranes, which, as a result of the specific nature of earphone sound reproduction topology, are forced to perpetually remain in the earphone sound reproduction topology's virtual remote *"kitchens"*.

TWELVE AXIOMS OF STEREOPRAVDA SPEARPHONE IEMS

StereoPravda performs this "teleportation" — as much as it's practically possible — first, by *optimizing* the cumulative sonic performance of all the IEMs' drivers in our earphone sound reproduction topology's virtual *loudspeakers* within our ear monitors' earphone sound reproduction topology's virtual *"living room"*, second, by *optimizing* their physical configuration to optimally couple them (both pneumatically and acoustically) to the tympanic membrane's native sonic response (taking into account the earphone sound reproduction topology's virtual *listener*'s physical location, the environment's pneumatic conditions and *his* or *her* hearing response) and, third, by *optimizing* IEMs' physical positioning to relocate the *loudspeakers* inside their bodies as close to the earphone sound reproduction topology's virtual *"kitchen"* — the ear canals' operational volume — as possible (and even inside of it).

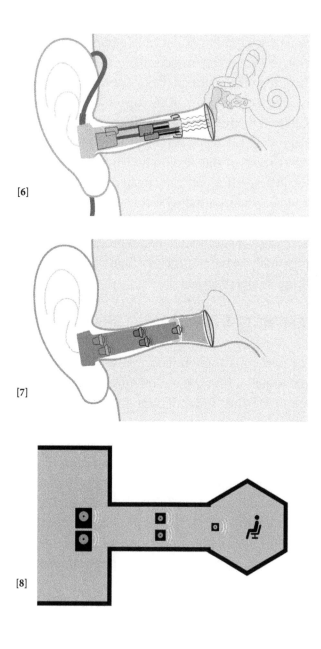

[6]

[7]

[8]

We accomplish this by bringing — again, as much as it is practically possible — all twelve *StereoPravda SPearphone IEMs Axioms* (which are the foundation of our ear monitors' design, their installation in the ear canals and the acoustical isolation methods as well as the capabilities of our dedicated electronics) fully in line with all twelve *Home High End Audio Axioms*.

The detailed description of our ear monitors' design and execution techniques below is used to show an example of a way for ear monitors' main aspects which define their sonic performance — their overall construction, acoustical isolation method and procedure for positioning in the anatomically typical ear canal — to jointly comply, to the extent that is practically possible, with all twelve *Home High End Audio Axioms* (using the same set of analogies as with the *Typical "Mid-Fi" IEMs Axioms*).

12 AXIOMS OF STEREOPRAVDA SPEARPHONE IEMs

STEREOPRAVDA SPEARPHONE AXIOM #1

As a result of the relocation of "naked" (i.e. lacking any sound tubes) key drivers' sound outlets at the very front of our earphones' body (*"listening room"*) and inside the operational volume of the ear canal (*"kitchen"*), we literally place these drivers *inside* the same space in which the eardrum (*listener*) is located [see the key driver position in Figure 6]*.

*Our Russian patent# 2 621 362; # 2 680 663
Our Russian utility model # 192 488

THIS, TO THE EXTENT THAT IT IS PRACTICALLY POSSIBLE, DOES COMPLY WITH THE *HOME HIGH END AUDIO* AXIOM #1

By not using sound tubes on the front key earphone drivers' sound outlets we *remove any obstacles* on the way of their sound propagation to the tympanic membrane, thus getting rid of any unwanted sound tube/sound bore resonances, which are virtually impossible to get rid of at a later stage of the electronic signal processing [SEE FIGURE 6].

With the secondary and auxiliary drivers located in the middle and at the back of our ear monitors, we are forced to compromise due to practical considerations and have no other option but to install sound tubes. But, with that said, with the goal of minimizing their negative impact on our ear monitors' sound quality, we make these sound tubes as wide and as short as possible. [SEE FIGURE 6].

By eliminating sound tubes on the key drivers and with the help of positioning our IEMs as deep as practically possible inside the ear canal, which ensures the minimum length (given the maximum diameter) of sound tubes for other speaker drivers, we get rid of — as much as it is practically possible — a large part of the signal distortions due to the input from these acoustic obstacles along the sound propagation path.

THIS, TO THE EXTENT THAT IT IS PRACTICALLY POSSIBLE, DOES COMPLY WITH THE HOME HIGH END AUDIO AXIOM #2

Additionally, due to their pronounced negative impact on overall sound quality, we categorically refuse to use the barrier acoustic filters in all of our ear monitors.

As we use mostly Balanced Armature drivers with the lowest resistance and relatively high sensitivity as the "naked" front key earphones' drivers, and because they are the closest to the tympanic membrane (*listener*), we thus ensure within the range of frequencies most critical for hearing their significant domination over the other earphone drivers in terms of sound intensity at the eardrum position.

Thus, using the above *"living room"/ kitchen"* analogy, *StereoPravda* can consider the task of "teleporting" the sonic character of the best home High End Audio systems — presumably transferred to the earphone sound reproduction topology's virtual *"living room"* of our ear monitors' body (for further developments please see below) — to be practically "teleported" to the earphone sound reproduction topology's virtual *listener*, who is permanently stuck in the earphone sound reproduction topology's virtual *"kitchen"* of the ear canal's operational volume:

— through the relocation of the key front drivers directly into the operational volume of the ear canal (*"kitchen"*), moreover — through their optimal positioning and orientation in that listening environment [SEE FIGURE 7];

THIS, TO THE EXTENT THAT IT IS PRACTICALLY POSSIBLE, DOES COMPLY WITH THE HOME HIGH END AUDIO AXIOM #2

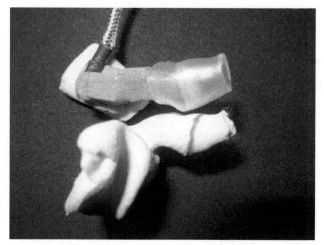

[9]

— through getting rid of — as much as possible — the "long, narrow, winding corridor" by straightening it considerably and reducing its length while significantly increasing its width (reducing the length and increasing the diameter of sound tubes) [SEE FIGURE 8];

THIS, TO THE EXTENT THAT IT IS PRACTICALLY POSSIBLE, DOES COMPLY WITH THE HOME HIGH END AUDIO AXIOM #2

— as well as through getting rid of the "thick curtain" at the *"living room"* entrance (due to the total absence of barrier acoustic filters in all of our ear monitors) [SEE FIGURE 8]*.

* Our Russian patent # 2 621 362; # 2 680 663
Our Russian utility model# 192 488

STEREOPRAVDA SPEARPHONE AXIOM #3

Due to the intended deep insertion of our ear monitor that will be positioned in the vicinity of the so-called Second Bend of the ear canal, that is, within several millimeter distance from the eardrums, and, additionally, on-axis with them, we have every chance to believe that the eardrums (*listener*) will *"see" directly in front of them* both "naked" sound outlets from key earphones' drivers positioned just outside of the *"living room"* of the earphones' body and the sound outlets from all the other ear monitors' drivers due to straight sound tubes from all the rest of the secondary and auxiliary drivers (because their axes are parallel not only to each other but also to the main vector of sound propagation in the ear canal, which is on-axis with the eardrum too) [SEE FIGURE 6]*.

THIS, TO THE EXTENT THAT IT IS PRACTICALLY POSSIBLE, DOES COMPLY WITH THE HOME HIGH END AUDIO AXIOM #3

* Our Russian patent # 2 621 362; # 2 680 663
Our Russian utility model# 192 488

Through their parallel arrangement, all of the drivers' radiation axes in our ear monitor designs achieve full conformity — in this aspect — with the typical construction of home loudspeakers of the highest caliber [SEE FIGURE 3]*.

*Our Russian patent # 2 621 362; # 2 680 663

THIS, TO THE EXTENT THAT IT IS PRACTICALLY POSSIBLE, DOES COMPLY WITH THE HOME HIGH END AUDIO AXIOM #4

Through the *deep insertion* of our earphones, positioned in the vicinity of the Second Bend of the ear canal [SEE FIGURE 9], and a special silicon tip's construction that seals the ear canal at this particular depth, we create *the most optimal* conditions for listening to the music in the *"kitchen"* of the IEMs' operational volume. These conditions are:

— *optimal* pneumatic coupling of the earphone drivers to the eardrum within the operational volume of the ear canal which is not only significantly smaller (compared to typical mid-fi IEMs) but also has a much simpler and more predictable shape (pneumatic coupling arises as a specific problem for IEMs' listening due to the ears being plugged; in home audio that is obviously not an issue at all);

— *optimal* acoustic coupling of the earphone drivers' acoustic outputs to the tympanic membrane within the operational volume; the smaller the volume,

THIS, TO THE EXTENT THAT IT IS PRACTICALLY POSSIBLE, DOES COMPLY WITH THE HOME HIGH END AUDIO AXIOM #5

and the simpler its shape the more easily it is to match the driver array's concrete physical output configuration to the tympanic membrane's typical frequency response mapping (*optimal* eardrum mapping matching arises as a specific problem for our IEMs front outlets' configuration due to the very close proximity of the drivers' acoustic outputs to the tympanic membrane; this clearly isn't a problem in home audio).

In any case, specific issues of isolating and installing IEMs notwithstanding, never mind the total absence of possibility to change the ear canal's physical configuration or to treat its walls acoustically, the minimal distance from the earphone drivers to the eardrums (*listener*) allows for a more accurate set-up of the overall physical configuration of all the drivers' acoustic outputs, both in terms of their position within the physical configuration of the ear canal's operational volume and the eardrum's position within it. Inside such a minimal operational volume of the ear canal it is much easier to get the drivers' total output *optimally* coupled to the typical mapping of the tympanic membrane's response (in the same sense as under an *optimal* "near field" positioning of the listener and the loudspeakers in the room, at such a close vicinity, their drivers' total output is much easier to get *optimally* matched to the listener's so called "open ears" response).*

THIS, TO THE EXTENT THAT IT IS PRACTICALLY POSSIBLE, DOES COMPLY WITH THE HOME HIGH END AUDIO AXIOM #5

* Our Russian patent# 2 621 362; # 2 680 663
  Our Russian utility model# 192 488

[10]

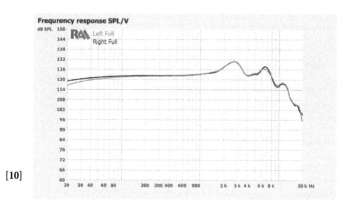

[11]

[12]

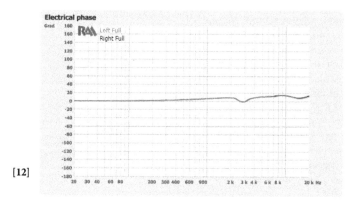

CHAPTER 7

STEREOPRAVDA SPEARPHONE AXIOM #6

As, given the correct installation of ear monitors, eardrums (*listener's two ears*) are always automatically positioned *equidistantly* from the right and the left channel ear monitors, it is self-evident that, in this aspect of IEM design and installation procedure, we are no different from everyone else, and do not have to take any additional actions*.

THIS DOES COMPLY WITH THE HOME HIGH END AUDIO AXIOM #6

* Sigh of relief …

STEREOPRAVDA SPEARPHONE AXIOM #7

Through the deep insertion of our IEMs we create conditions for *significant* dominance of the intensity of the direct sound from "naked" key drivers not only over the intensity of all sorts of acoustic resonances and reflections within the operational volume of the ear canal ("*kitchen*"), exaggerated by a shallow insertion, but also over the intensity of the acoustic contribution from other drivers located in the middle and in the back of our IEMs [SEE FIGURE 7].

THIS, TO THE EXTENT THAT IT IS PRACTICALLY POSSIBLE, DOES COMPLY WITH THE HOME HIGH END AUDIO AXIOM #7

Furthermore, compared to shallow earphone's insertion, deep insertion of ear monitors to be positioned in the vicinity of the ear canal's Second Bend brings a significant reduction of the ear canal "occlusion" effect and decrease the degree of the "bone conduction" to the middle ear.

[13]

[14]

It is should be clear by now that only by inserting the IEMs deeply enough to isolate the ear canal around its Second Bend, where its walls' cartilage tissue abruptly changes to the bone (you can easily see the transition line at the earmolds) you can significantly reduce both the ear canal's "occlusion" effect and the "bone conduction" of the sound to the middle ear. At the same time, due to the typical human anatomy, such IEMs' positioning would place its drivers as close to the tympanic membrane as practically possible. The combination of these four factors — optimal pneumatic coupling to the tympanic membrane, reduced "occlusion" effect, decreased "bone conduction" and the closest distance to the eardrums — would create the best acoustic and aural conditions for the earphone listening as it would resemble optimal *"near field"* acoustic conditions for listening to the music at home as closely as practically possible.

Which is the fundamental goal we set for the *StereoPravda* SPearphone IEMs project from its very inception, and this goal is behind all our main proprietary IEMs' solutions: the overall design of our ear monitors, the method of their installation inside the ear canal and a proper way to seal it*.

* Our Russian patent# 2 621 362; # 2 680 663
Our Russian utility model# 192 488

THIS, TO THE EXTENT THAT IT IS PRACTICALLY POSSIBLE, DOES COMPLY WITH THE HOME HIGH END AUDIO AXIOM #7

Due to the deep insertion of our IEMs, we can position all the drivers in our ear monitors (*loudspeakers*) — as closely as possible to — and on-axis with — the eardrums (*listener*) [SEE FIGURE 6].

Another sound quality improvement opportunity provided by deep insertion relates to the so-called "main vector of sound propagation within the ear canal": in case of *StereoPravda* ear monitors it is (virtually) parallel to all the axes of all the drivers' sound radiation patterns [SEE FIGURES 6 AND 7]*.

THIS, TO THE EXTENT THAT IT IS PRACTICALLY POSSIBLE, DOES COMPLY WITH THE HOME HIGH END AUDIO AXIOM #8

* Our Russian patent # 2 621 362; # 2 680 663

By applying appropriate Balanced Armature drivers and corresponding sound tube properties (physical dimensions, materials, installation methods, etc.) as well as through the careful selection of corresponding matching resistors and the application of our proprietary silicone tip design we are able to achieve a close similarity between the amplitude and frequency response characteristics of our ear monitors and the general overall shape of typical amplitude and frequency characteristics of the "open ear response".

THIS, TO THE EXTENT THAT IT IS PRACTICALLY POSSIBLE, DOES COMPLY WITH THE HOME HIGH END AUDIO AXIOM #9

[FIGURE 10 depicts the frequency response of the *StereoPravda* SPearphone SB-7 ear monitors, while FIGURE 11 — albeit, on a very different scale — shows the typical frequency response of the "open ear"; the graphs are courtesy of, respectively, Roman Kuznetzov of *reference-audio-analyzer.pro and interfidelity.com/SourceInterlinkMedia*]

Conformity of the IEMs' response with the "open ear response" could be one of the possible reasons for the subjective feeling that our earphones' sound presentation seems to be located just outside the head.

THIS, TO THE EXTENT THAT IT IS PRACTICALLY POSSIBLE, DOES COMPLY WITH THE HOME HIGH END AUDIO AXIOM #9

The similarity of the curves in FIGURES 10 AND 11 is, naturally, purely nominal and like all such routine measurements in audio does not prove anything conclusively. However, according to the general opinion of those who auditioned our ear monitors, they really do demonstrate a considerable effect of a static "outside the head" hearing experience*.

* Our Russian patent # 2 621 362; # 2 680 663
Our Russian utility model# 192 488

By meticulously selecting the drivers for each *StereoPravda* earphone model, choosing their assembled in-band arrays' physical configurations, the drivers' acoustic loading formats and the arrays' in-band matching resistors, we achieve the optimal IEMs' responses *without* the use of any electrical "passive" crossover filter networks per se.

Using only matching resistors and *completely refusing* to use both electrical "passive" crossover filters and wide-band barrier acoustic filters allows us to fully get rid of the problems inherent in almost all typical mid-fi IEMs/CIEMs; in particular, to avoid significant phase shifts [this is proven by the phase characteristics of our *StereoPravda* SPearphone SB-7 in-ear monitors, which lie at an almost zero degree phase shift along the whole range of sonic frequencies — see FIGURE 12; the graph is courtesy of Roman Kuznetzov of reference-audio-analyzer.pro]*.

THIS, TO THE EXTENT THAT IT IS PRACTICALLY POSSIBLE, DOES COMPLY WITH THE HOME HIGH END AUDIO AXIOM #10

* This aspect of our earphones' design is — probably more so than any of the others — deeply related to our unfaltering adherence to the fundamental principle of designing High End Audio equipment — *maximum simplicity of design with the highest possible quality of its execution*.

Thanks to the conformity of our ear monitors' design with the possibility of using them in a *two-way "active"* mode with the *StereoPravda* DACCA two-way "active" dedicated portable processor/amplifier (which provides a suit of special adjustments on board), we expect to be getting the absolute-level sound quality when using this fully portable no-holds-barred IEMs portable audio system [SEE FIGURE 13].

THIS, TO THE EXTENT THAT IT IS PRACTICALLY POSSIBLE, DOES COMPLY WITH THE HOME HIGH END AUDIO AXIOM #11

To achieve the best sound quality possible in our products we use the best "passive" components (electrical, mechanical and others). For instance, the matching resistors we use in our IEMs are of "audiophile grade" quality, they are made in France by *Holco* and are widely used in home audio equipment of the highest caliber.

The *Black Cat Cable*'s Pravda 32 connecting cable in *StereoPravda* ear monitors is specially designed for this particular application and custom-made for us in the US by our long-term partner and "cable guru" Chris Sommovigo (of *Illuminati/Stereovox/ Stereolab/Black Cat Cable* fame).

THIS, TO THE EXTENT THAT IT IS PRACTICALLY POSSIBLE, DOES COMPLY WITH THE HOME HIGH END AUDIO AXIOM #12

As with any components we use all of their mechanical properties and durability have been developed to explicitly conform with the priority of attaining sound of the highest quality possible. This is why we use connecting cable of the highest caliber for our ear monitors, as its properties fully comply with the highest cable manufacturing standards of Home High End Audio [SEE FIGURE 14].

Our choice of electrical "contact group" for the standard TRS mini-jack connector was also driven by that same priority. In order to implement the whole IEMs' input signal interface, which includes the TRS contact group, our connecting cable and the appropriate matching resistors connected to it, we had to come up with a special assembly procedure, which also required the manufacturing of a custom-made casing for the whole "mini-jack" connector [SEE FIGURE 14].

THIS, TO THE EXTENT THAT IT IS PRACTICALLY POSSIBLE, DOES COMPLY WITH THE HOME HIGH END AUDIO AXIOM #12

It is worth noting here that the only existing IEMs driver technology that allows us to achieve the goal to (virtually) fully comply with all twelve *Home High End Audio Axioms* stated above is the earphone multi-driver and multi-way technology which is based on using the *Balanced Armature* drivers (aka BA drivers).

It is important to clarify here that our definition of audio systems as *portable* includes their two main features: first, not only the obvious portability of this audio system class, but also, crucially, their enhanced ability to *isolate* the listener's hearing from external noise. Because the vast majority of the best headphones are usually of the *"open-back"* type (meaning that their design principle presupposes a complete lack of the acoustical isolation), audio systems based on the use of such headphones cannot, according to this definition, be considered "portable." Whereas all "*closed-back*" headphones, which do provide a certain level of noise isolation (usually much lower than most typical IEMs), generally remain to this day "second-rate" in terms of their sound quality — mostly because the general headphones' sonic problems are even more exacerbated by the very strong "can" resonances of their body's closed cavity.

The sound quality of BA drivers is amazingly high for their diminutive size. As they were developed for the audiological industry's applications, much more "serious" than mere consumer electronics' ones, they are much more sophisticated devices with very precise tolerances than typical drivers to be used for consumer earphones, and possibly due to that provenance the BA drivers sonic properties closely match the typical eardrum acoustic response. This is exactly why, when implementing our plans we chose the technology of multi-driver multi-way assembly from BA driver arrays, which is the only currently available headphone or IEMs/ CIEMs technology that allows us to achieve full compliance with both our definition of the "portable" audio systems and, at the same time, all twelve *Home High End Audio Axioms*.

Were one, for the sake of clarity, to generalize all of the specific technologies and solutions we employ in our ear monitors (described in full in our Russian patent # 2 621 362 and our Russian utility model # 192 488) — describing how they fit into the overall concept — the most fundamental of them can be summarized in the following list:

12 STEPS OF CONCRETE SOLUTIONS TO DEVELOP
STEREOPRAVDA SPEARPHONE IEMs

(in the order in which they were implemented)

1 The choice of sonically optimal *multi-driver* and *multi-way* BA driver arrays and proprietary technologies of assembling them into finished ear monitors as the main guiding principle of our IEMs' construction.

2 A *deep insertion* of the ear monitors in the vicinity of the Second Bend of the ear canals and acoustical isolation at the IEMs' front.

3 A special design of the universal silicone tips (proprietary shape, a special two-dimensional tilt of the tips, controlled "leakage" of acoustic isolation to prevent excessive pneumatic pressure build up, etc.).

4 A careful selection and corresponding arrangement of key drivers without any sound tubes (i.e. "naked" key drivers).

5 *Parallel* arrangement of all speaker driver radiation pattern axes, with their common axis parallel to the main vector of sound propagation within the ear canal.

6 A special selection of the nomenclature of secondary and auxiliary drivers, as well as developing the elements of their acoustic loading.

7 Developing the layout and physical configuration specifics of every separate driver array.

8 Developing the overall design and layout specifics of the in-ear monitor as a whole (achieving a special physical configuration of the assembled unit with the goal of maximum conforming to the typical anatomy of the ear canal around its Second Bend, taking into account its anatomical feature called the Inter-Tragal Notch, as well as ensuring that all the corresponding positioning specifics of the design within the typical ear canal are on-axis with the eardrum and closely match its acoustic response mapping, etc. — SEE FIGURE 9).

9 Absolute refusal to use any simplified traditional electrical "passive" filter networks for our IEMs.

10 Absolute refusal to use any barrier acoustic filters for our IEMs.

11 Designing and building a *two-way "active"* dedicated *StereoPravda* DACCA fully differential digital-to-analog DAC/crossover/tonecontrol/ amplifier unit for our IEMs' significantly improved performance when used in the "active" mode.

12 The joint development of connecting cable for our ear monitors with Chris Sommovigo of *Black Cat Cable* over numerous iterations, as well as implementation of a specially selected "OEM" TRS mini-jack connector "group" while applying our own proprietary technology for installing all the TRS mini-jack hardware with the matching resistors inside of the custom-made connector chassis.

The final result of using all of these twelve solutions can be seen in Figure **15**, which depicts the fully assembled *StereoPravda* SPearphone SB-7, while Figure **16** shows its internal construction (this 3-D rendering picture of SB-7 is courtesy of Stephen Ambrose and Cole Hammer of *Asius Technologies*).

Naturally, compared to the most high-quality home stereo systems, we are still a long way removed from a full "holography" of sound in such "static" portable systems, as a fully three-dimensional "dynamic" sonic presentation under portable conditions requires not only the application of advanced head trackers (to monitor head movements with a sufficiently high resolution in space and time), individual and used transducers' calibrations, but also very powerful DSP processors which would run some highly sophisticated software in real time[2].

Nevertheless, almost full compliance on *StereoPravda*'s part with all twelve *Home High End Audio Axioms* allows any user of our equipment to clearly feel a pronounced "open ear" effect,

---

[2] E.g. the *Smyth Research* "Realizer."

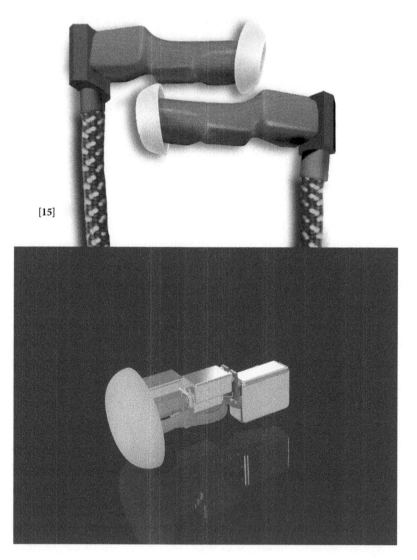

[15]

[16]

manifesting itself in the static escape of the sound stage (however, on a correspondingly smaller scale) outside the head with fully focused "solid" musical images — akin to home stereo systems of the highest caliber.

In case of our *StereoPravda* SPearphone ear monitors, a scrupulous adherence to all twelve of the Home High End Audio Axioms evidently became a necessary condition for passing the torch of old home High End Audio sonic traditions to the new generation of "portable" audiophiles. While the combination of devoted resources, determination in searching for and implementing the best specific solutions and — last but not least — the luck that accompanied the development process, have eventually allowed us to meet the goal..

Following only some of the *Axioms* listed above would clearly not be sufficient for reaching it.

As they say, "being somewhat free is like being slightly pregnant." The High End Audio's "absolute" sonic pretensions place its results in a "binary" fashion because a complete implementation of an "absolute" idea can take one of only two available discrete states, and it is clear what they are...

In order to understand and fully appreciate the nature of our ear monitors, it is important to be aware of the fact that a given solution — no matter how peculiar — is never the goal in itself, but a part of a whole, a part of a grand design and the means of reaching some sort of a bifurcation point, at which a leap in quality of music reproduction occurs.

100% OPTIMALITY VERSUS 100% UNIVERSALITY

Without re-thinking from scratch the conventional ear monitor design achieving a sonic presentation typical for music reproduction of the highest quality at home, on a portable platform, would simply be impossible.

The example of our ear monitors is merely used here to clearly show the futility of quantitative attempts of improving the design of typical mid-fi IEMs/CIEMs, which the vast majority of players in the ear monitors industry is currently engaged in, to skyrocket them to the High End Audio-dom as well as to give an example of how formulating the goal differently requires a very specific set of sufficiently unorthodox solutions. Were we to use conventional orthodox methods, we would never have achieved the goals we had set for ourselves.

Similarly, a fundamental improvement of old-school High End Audio's performance cannot materialize merely through the use of tired methods and technologies: it is only attainable by using sufficiently unorthodox approaches and solutions. Although, only time will tell what those are[3].

Unfortunately, the need for change that is proclaimed by the audio industry as a whole is accompanied by the intent to "change everything while changing nothing" at the level of its individual players.

Thus, all of the details from the tables above are only used to illustrate one of many valid ideas for ensuring the continuity of home High End Audio's ideals in today's conditions. Besides, they show a way to keep on to consistently observing all of its fundamental technical principles. At the same time they demonstrate the flip side of this issue — how (and possibly why) not only the mass-market manufacturers but even the mid-fi companies are not capable to strive for the "absolute."

---

[3] Although some very promising novel technologies already exist — for instance, advanced digital processors for fine-tuning loudspeakers by correcting the inherent crossover problems in them and reducing the listening room's effect on their sound by the Australian company *Deqx*; but unfortunately such progressive technologies still remain marginal due to the overall industry's inertia and its indifference, if not overt hostility, to everything that is truly innovative.

The main demarcation line between true High End Audio equipment and mass-produced or mid-fi fare lies in the sphere of a manufacturer's (and/or other "links in the chain" from them to the customers) priority choice: either maximum 100% optimality in terms of sound quality of the products on the one hand or maximum 100% universality — aimed at maximizing the averaged "physical and all the other comfort" of the products' use — on the other.

When I demonstrated the first prototypes of our *StereoPravda* SPearphone SB-7 ear monitors to the person who initially planted the theme of superior quality multi-driver/multi-way ear monitors into public consciousness and eventually commercialized the idea on a grand scale, **Jerry Harvey**, at the *RMAF-2016* show in Denver, he not only responded with something like "*a very nice voicing,*" but also added — somewhat jealously — that he himself started his operation with developing BA driver assemblies similar to the ones used in SB-7.

He could be right — but even so, after this initial stage our research and development paths diverged drastically...

As any company that is counting on unstoppable growth does, his firm, *Ultimate Ears*[4], moved in the direction of 100% universality of its products — i.e. toward designs that let each product provide all 100 percent of averaged comfort to all 100 percent of potential consumers in the market. With that in mind, Jerry pioneered the Custom IEMs technology, abbreviated to CIEMs, meaning the use of individual molds of the listener's ear canals as the outer shells for ear monitors. Naturally, this involved sacrificing their 100% sonic optimality[5] while doing so.

---

[4] Subsequently sold to *Logitech* for tens of millions of dollars, with Jerry then starting another successful company, *Jerry Harvey Audio*.

[5] Which — as any individual sample of a finished product of this kind is by definition always singular, while the range of physical configurations of individual user molds, in which a particular model's speaker driver complements are arranged in varying physical configurations — negates the invariance of the possible "optimality" for a given model. Optimality is a binary concept: it's either fully realized or not at all.

Among other things, the list of features implemented in the CIEMs' design to ensure full "universality" through the 100 percent comfort of his "custom" earphone models for the 100 percent of potential customers in the market implied, as one of the fundamental principles, the lack of any openly admitted routines that are related to regular technical maintenance (although BA drivers, like all the others, have a tendency to fail sooner or later, meaning that the promised 100 percent of comfort from their supposed perpetual use can, at any point, be ruined by the discomfort of the necessity to repair the ear monitors — although, naturally, no one draws the users' attention to the possibility of this course of events).

Whereas *StereoPravda* went in the opposite direction: fully aware of the limited possibilities in terms of unstoppable growth, we moved towards a full sonic 100% *optimality* of our ear monitors. Naturally, sacrificing their 100% market appeal "universality" in the process.

Thus our concept of optimality with the necessary sacrifice of universality[6], includes as one of its main tenets the earphones' regular maintenance, akin regular car maintenace (the latter is, naturally, taboo for all consumer electronics manufacturers, who would rather not see or hear from their customers until their next purchase).

Can you imagine how "optimal" the performance of a car would be without its regular scheduled maintenance? And even if its potential customer would have been delighted to get rid of the nuisance of regular scheduled maintenance procedures, what kind of car that would be? Would it have to be built like a tank and moving at 50 mph speed maximum? Then who would buy such a monster?

Or, the opposite alternative — a disposable car, is it really a viable option? I don't think so. That is why the inconvenience of

---

[6] By our estimates, around 15-20 percent of potential customers really do fail our "physical examination" for the comfortable use of the SB-7 (in which case, by the way, our SB-5 or the SB-3.5 models could possibly offer a comfortable alternative).

regularly scheduled maintenance procedures allows us to have the modern cars with their exceptional performance. The same is true for the level of sonic performance of earphones — you can't really achieve the best sound quality that can be with, practically speaking, disposable products which do not require regular maintenance procedures.

The reason I mention regular maintenance procedures is because this aspect, avoided by mid-fi manufacturers at all costs, allows *StereoPravda* to implement the necessary set of solutions for our ear monitor design, which, without regular maintenance of our products, we would have never been able to realize.

To reiterate one more time, considering the fact that the products of Jerry Harvey's current company — *Jerry Harvey Audio* — are in the upper segments of the ear monitor market (although these mainly are IEMs/CIEMs for professional use by musicians on stage) as well as the fact that the principles of these designs fully comply with the aforementioned *Axioms of Typical "Mid-Fi" IEMs*, and, at the same time, do not comply with the whole set of *Home High End Audio Axioms* above, it will not be an exaggeration to state again the following: the portable audio transducer industry — both in Jerry's case and overall — still remains somewhere around the mid-fi stage of its development. And truly high-end companies, with the appropriate pedigree and the torch of venerable audiophile traditions in their hands, are just beginning to appear on the horizon…

'FROM A SPARK A FIRE WILL GROW!'

The history of many old-school home High End Audio manufacturers has always been marked by their unceasing attempts to rid themselves of a feeling of claustrophobia, inevitably arising as a result of the very limited appeal of their products to the overall audio market, which, especially lately, has been constantly shrinking and come to rely almost exclusively on momentary and often very unpredictable whims of the current audiophile community (e.g. cassette tape deck renaissance).

Despite some examples of questionable and ultimately failed attempts at a wider market appeal (like when, back in the 1990s, *Krell* attempted to get the erotic flicks hunk Fabio to promote its products — quite possibly the least appropriate person for a celebrity endorsement of this kind) only a handful of High End Audio companies have been able to pull it off. For example, when the equipment from exclusive audio salons ended up (for entirely random reasons) in the houses of people that, while wealthy, were very far removed from a deep passion not just for audio, but even for music itself.

The pinnacle of success in this area were those rare occasions of gaining widespread "fame" when large automobile manufacturers (such as *Lexus, Acura* and *Bentley*) licensed the names of these companies (*Mark Levinson, Krell* and *Burmester*) for the audio systems in their vehicles.

As for the rare attempts of high-end manufacturers to expand their sales market by entering large consumer electronics retail chains, they always ended in nothing (e.g. *Parasound* tried to be sold in *Good Guys* chain's stores and had to withdraw from it having lost most of their loyal High End Audio dealers in process) for a range of obvious reasons, the main of which was the egregious scarcity of consumers for such products and, therefore, these goods' extreme detachment "from the demands of common people."

Nevertheless, the path to expanding their market appeal activity for those companies that made such attempts (all of them of the "garage" category at their inception) has always started with establishing a reputation in the enthusiasts community. This initial success could subsequently be extended somewhat beyond the strictly audiophile market.

As for the unique achievement of *Bang & Olufsen*[7] in its prime, with their eye on significant sales in the elite segment of audio technology for "ordinary" people, no one else was able to replicate it in the home High End Audio industry. Furthermore, numerous similar attempts to take the elite segments of the audio market by storm by such giants from South-East Asia as *Sony, Samsung* and others, have also failed, time and time again.

Likewise, all shots of manufacturers of home High End Audio at direct sales in the market for "luxury" lifestyle products have always ended up in a complete fiasco.

The main reason why this happens is closely related to the general system of values and priorities of the affluent public in relation to the effort, time, money and, most importantly, square feet of living space (what's more, generally with no interest in the subject matter), which would inevitably enter the conversation in the context of the principal functionality of High End Audio.

It is precisely for the reason of the pervasive scarcity of these "square feet" — "the rich also cry" — that the prospects of entering the "luxury" lifestyle market look far more promising for the portable audio version of High End Audio compared to the home audio one.

Nevertheless, this market penetration, as is the case with home audio, is likely to become a reality only after earning an initial

---

[7] Strictly speaking, B&O has no relation whatsoever to High End Audio, as their main concept, concrete technical solutions, industrial design, as well as marketing almost never suggested even barely noticeable correlation with the aforementioned key functionality and utility of High End Audio. Nevertheless, not long ago, were one to even mention high performance audio subject to almost anybody, they would immediately exclaim: "Of course, I know what you're talking about — you're talking about Bang and Olufsen, right?"

reputation among enthusiasts that are fully committed to the audiophile cause.

It is worth noting that — because of the focus of portable audio products on personal use — one of the fundamental obstacles to the spread of home High End Audio systems throughout its history, the *Wife Acceptance Factor*, is removed from the consideration entirely.

Any attempt of High End Audio products to enter "luxury" lifestyle markets has always put them in a vulnerable position: these markets, despite the veneer of perfection and quality, usually operate on the notion of offering the appropriate status-symbols as the main priority. Thus the supposed intellectual component of luxury lifestyle products is, with only rare exceptions (such as elite restaurants, spirits, cigars and the like), reduced to a bare minimum.

Successful positioning of luxury lifestyle products always requires not only a fortunate turn of events but also a long-term, consistent and prohibitively expensive strategy. For audio of the highest caliber this strategy has to be considered from a whole multitude of commitments, including an open recognition of the educational function and a corresponding practical utility inherent in High End Audio, an implementation of all the latest shifts in technology, an acknowledgement of all the demography, economics, and lifestyle changes, and in full compliance with the current socio-political and cultural contexts in which increasing demand for mindfulness among potential customers should be fully taken into account.

Deep interest in music has always existed and will always exist. And the home version of High End Audio will, undoubtedly, remain in demand — although, naturally not to the extent that it was a quarter of a century ago during its Golden Age.

One of the most obvious opporutnities for High End Audio industry, currently experiencing a period of significant decline as a result of completely ignoring all of the fundamental global changes and demands, is to capitalize on the "spark" of portable High End Audio, from which, given the right approach and right circumstances, to quote that *bona fide* revolutionary V. I. Lenin, a "fire will grow!"

I do not only mean the rapid spread of portable audio products of the highest sonic performance within the significantly transformed high performance audio enthusiasts' community (that can still benefit directly or indirectly the dedicated home audio's overall sales), but also an active drifting of such devices into all kinds of parallel markets. Markets that up until now are very distant from the true audiophile passion and that remained — and still remain — indifferent, due to all the reasons discussed above, to truly "serious" audio products.

Chapter 8. What is the cause of 'Audio Alpinism'?

L ooking at the history of unceasing discoveries, inventions, innovations in audio technology and adjacent fields through an imaginary telescope, one can only make out the contours of the High End Audio industry through a corresponding "microscope."

Nevertheless, the internal fascination of the peaks of audio continues to put a spell on millions of people all over the world, at times giving their fascination the trappings of a true obsession.

In 1943 American psychologist Abraham Maslow published his famous book, *A Theory of Human Motivation*, which introduced the notion of humans as beings that possess a hierarchy of needs.

"This hierarchy of needs usually manifests itself in the shape of a pyramid. At its foundation — our primary needs, i.e. the basics of our physiological survival (such as food, air and water), as well as security (such as law, order and stability). The level above is our need for love and close relationships. Another level higher, we get to our need for growth and

development — the possibility of attaining our own goals, of mastering knowledge and skills, of having our achievements and successes acknowledged. And, finally, at the very peak of the pyramid is our desire of what Maslow was the first in calling 'SELF-ACTUALIZATION', i.e. the achievement of happiness by following moral ideals and using one's own creative powers for the sake of creativity itself." [1]

Moreover, all the needs are interconnected, with each existing in a state of constant interaction with the others, ensuring the stability of the whole structure, and each next level corresponds to the progressive development stages of a mature human being.

The expression "to have one's mind on higher things" is fully congruent with Maslow's model, which is why mentioning his theories at the end of a view of High End Audio, is, in my opinion, highly useful, no matter how simple the parallels appear to be. Especially if one assumes that every level of human needs in his model is catered to by appropriate audio equipment.

As, at first glance, my own biography in audio is rife with paradox and do not fully align with Maslow's classic pyramid, I have always wanted to figure out where the *catch* is. What's more, I have no doubt that my own motivation to devote myself wholly to High End Audio contains a number of traits common for all audiophiles.

For instance, were one to accept Maslow's original model, it follows that, throughout all these years, my volunteer audio journalism[2], even if one writes it off as a need for the "highest" quest

---

[1] Quoted from Atul Gawande's book, *Being Mortal (and translated from Russian)*.

[2] Throughout decades of publishing in Russian specialised audio magazines, I have never received a single payment. Ironically, only once did a local distributor commission me to write a feature for his audio forum, and paid me generously upfront. However, after reading the material … he never published it.

for self-actualization, has not only failed to help me realize my more mundane basic needs but, what's more, hindered me in every way imaginable. The same can be said about the efforts and resources spent on gradually upgrading my own audio systems.

Which of my needs, then, did my paradoxical obsession with High End Audio help to satisfy, according to Maslow's theory (except creative self-actualization)?

Going through different answers to this question, I contemplated the possible contributions of each of the possible pyramid levels to my sonic aspirations — but, juxtaposing them with contradicting motivations from different levels, I failed to see enough of an explanation for such a prolonged and "possessed" state of my mind.

And because for a long time I could not find a clear answer to the question above, I had the longstanding impression that something was wrong with Maslow's original pyramid after all.

Clearly, the current location of the pyramid's centre of gravity (i.e. the epicentre of our most pressing motivations) significantly changes with time, it doesn't remain static. It also depends on the goals that we (explicitly or implicitly) set for our future development, planning how "high" up the pyramid we will need to climb, and seeing how high we have climbed *already*.

Looking at my audio biography one can see that instead of pushing my pyramid's centre of gravity down towards the material manifestation of success and stability I still wanted irresistibly to upset its balance by pulling it upwards.

At my advanced age my "ascent" along Maslow's levels has reached its peak but the desire to keep moving on up still remains after thirty years of being preoccupied with High End Audio, and the question arises: is following moral ideas and creativity for creativity's sake (i.e. self-actualization) truly the top of the pyramid? Or not yet?

Maybe there is something else, something higher than merely the universal need for self-actualization?

Thirty-five years before the publication of Maslow's research, Harvard philosopher Josiah Royce published his *Philosophy of Loyalty*, in which he tried to figure out why — "just a" — fully comfortable existence seems empty and meaningless to many people. What else do we need to feel like our life is filled with meaning?

The answer to that question, according to Royce, lies in the notion that the need for this meaning exists in everyone, yet we search for it somewhere beyond our own selves. He called this adherence to a fundamental external meaning *loyalty*. He saw it as the antipode to individualism.

However, Royce hated militant individualism. He wrote:

"... Human beings need loyalty as if it were air. It does not necessarily lead to happiness and may even involve suffering but we all need something bigger than ourselves for our life to become bearable. Without this we are governed by our desires, which are transient, capricious and insatiable. Ultimately, they only bring pain... Every moment of a person's internal existence is a transition from one impulse to the next... As we cannot see a light within ourselves, let us try and look for it outside." [3]

Contemporary psychologists replaced Royce's "loyalty" (in short, something larger than ourselves outside of us) with the notion of *"transcendence."* And then they have added another level of motivation on the top of Maslow's pyramid, above the level of self-actualisation — *the need for transcendence.*

---

[3] Quoted from Atul Gawande's book, *Being Mortal (and translated from Russian)*.

This addition occurred due to — among other things — the fact that the last decades saw significant improvements in the scientific understanding of the natural successive development stages of a full-fledged and mature individual. Despite an ideological resistance from militant individualists, all scientific facts support the model of human development in which the final stage is completed in the formation of an individual need for genuine compassion towards others through the process of transcendence.

Curiously I have so far only been able to find the picture of the English version of the upgraded Maslow pyramid with transcendence at the top, while all of the Russian versions are outdated: all of them still end (hardly by accident) at the level of self-actualization (especially relevant for the continuing "troubled" times our country is going through).

By the way, having spent many years — cumulatively — abroad, I gradually began to realize — even if examples were rare — that the more mature of Maslow's models, with the transcendence peak, truly does restore the correct notions of the direction in which our civilization would do well to move in. It turns out there is still a lot of room for improvement all over the world. And this realization finally allowed me to understand many of the peculiarities of my audio biography.

Unfortunately, this path is always thorny…

Therefore, despite the presence of the transcendence peak in the "imported" version of the pyramid, I never had any illusions about how densely the pyramid's top is populated in any country — this fact has the same level of bitterness everywhere. Dissecting what the specific twists of these transcendental needs are and what shape their satisfaction should take can only be done on one's own. In my case, it so happened that I chose the means of scaling the heights of High End Audio for this mission.

A friend of mine from Saint Petersburg called me not too long ago and asked a question about an outstanding — in his opinion — audio product: "What is it — the result of the manufacturer's conscious actions or a fortunate accident? And, in case it is the latter, what an inexperienced audiophile is supposed to do? How is he supposed to see such a masterpiece in the cornucopia of seemingly similar products?"

To that I replied: "The very fact that you are calling me with this question explains a lot. I brought this product to your attention. I have known its manufacturer for many years as an honest person, well-versed in all things audio, with a very high level of professionalism which he is constantly proving. But all of these are merely the necessary conditions for your attention to be drawn to this product among many others like it. And do you know which condition is sufficient? My genuine long-time friendship with its manufacturer and my genuine long-time friendship with you. Neither one is born by accident but because, throughout many years, time and time again, we had the opportunity to make sure that we are not only good friends who think alike, but are also fulfilling the needs of the same level with the help of audio."

Another example of the use of Maslow's pyramid in its sonic version (this time — for determining the level of aspiration for the best sound quality of various hardware) will, I think, also be highly illustrative.

The positioning of a given product at one of the pyramid's levels is determined by the level of the manufacturer's needs that are being satisfied with its production. This also holds true for the product's distributors and dealers, as well as potential customers. Thus the level of the needs of everyone involved determines the level of the pyramid at which they will all meet. Consequently, the pyramid level is not correlated with the product's manufacturing cost and price but with the original intent of everyone involved.

When the word "sublime" is used to describe an experience of moral or spiritual purity elevated to the highest (sic!) degree, it is in complete accordance with Maslow's model. Which is why a discussion of the latter in the context of High End Audio allows to put the contents of this book in a proper perspective and draw two important conclusions. First, that a very pinnacle of primal human needs exists and, second, that they can only be satisfied when dealing with a partner that is trying to satisfy needs at the same level of the pyramid. Providing appropriate audio equipment for ascending to the very top of the pyramid is the *raison d'être* of true High End Audio.

It is not in vain that I have repeatedly mentioned the need to understand the internal motivation at various industry levels, including the human level. This information is hardly available from official channels and is usually only transmitted along friendship chains — as in the example with my friend. But only with its help will an audio component or system occupy the appropriate level in the sonic hierarchy: somewhere between the "skies" of supreme creative achievement and the "ground" of primitive utilitarianism.

The same can be said about the positioning on this pyramid of the needs of potential hardware consumers whose personal needs can only be satisfied with the help of manufacturers positioned on the corresponding level. As a rule, the sale of such hardware, as well as the search for it usually arises from such primal needs, not vice versa. Therefore, without a clear idea of the primal needs that have to be satisfied on both sides of the equation through the use of certain equipment there'll be only confusion.

At every level of the audio pyramid like needs to meet like. Meaning that a product that arose from an irresistible vital need on the part of the manufacturer, distributed by a dealer that finds himself at that same level as a result of the same needs, has to find its way to the target clientele located at the same level in the hierarchy of needs.

Sometimes someone on either side of the "sales barricades", makes a futile attempt to skip over several levels of the pyramid, to go "from rags to riches" by positioning themselves at an undeservedly high level of personal needs. As numerous examples show, this usually ends badly (for one of the sides involved, at least).

Only if created and offered at the very top of the pyramid, at the level of transcendental need's satisfaction, does hardware — no matter how inexpensive — find its soul and become true High End Audio.

Very few reach this transcendence peak, and good intentions are necessary — but insufficient condition — so should one really be surprised how rare the examples of it really are, how rarely it manifests, and how infrequently one participates in a truly high-end demonstration?

Personally I have been fortunate enough to hear what High End Audio is actually capable of only a handful of times in my life. And a large part of this book is dedicated to explaining why this happens so rarely. Nevertheless, from time to time, it really does happen...

My own audio biography can also serve as a decent example of the validity of the principles behind the of Maslow's pyramid, topped with the transcendence peak, which justify my inner drive for further ascent and explain the seeming contradictions and peculiarities of my audio writing.

I can definitely say that, as a side effect from fulfilling my own transcendental needs by writing about audio many specific questions found answers in my work that would have never been found if their examination took place at a different, lower level of need fulfillment.

I remember how at one of the press-conferences at the Stereophile magazine's exhibition in Los Angeles many years ago one of the editors was asked the question to which he could only reply: "I don't know what to tell you as I have never written about this yet." It only remains to add that the contents of what is written will depend heavily on the level of the pyramid of needs at which one will be looking for the answers.

To continue to be professionally engaged in high performance audio today one has no choice but to return to its roots and the fundamental ideas of its "forefathers." Meaning to once again engage — in different guises — in the transcendental scaling of its heights as its original mission of fulfillment of the highest needs, which constituted the very essence of High End Audio and allowed to — although in recent years, thanks to inertia more than anything else — reap the harvest from this field for many decades.

And if someone attempts this, he or she will undoubtedly have to employ algorithms for promoting sound (*sic!*) ideas that are drastically different from the ones universally taken for granted now. And the word "*good*" in the phrase "to write a good review" will need to take on an entirely new meaning, not the one we are used to today.

I am sure that a certain number of readers will be perplexed yet again: why dwell on such abstract and often personal issues at all? Why not get straight to the point?

Maslow proved with his research that as long as a person has not fulfilled his most basic needs, including the need for education, the higher ones — forming an aesthetic taste and self-actualization — will not arise. Thus it would be premature to discuss the details of the ascent to the very peak of his augmented pyramid.

Therefore without first making sure that someone understands the fundamental reasons for his or her obsession with high performance audio it is entirely futile to speak of using it to satisfy their transcendental needs. The result of using High End Audio without being fully aware of its *raison d'être* will always be inadequate.

Skipping the key stage of comprehending "the point of it all," getting straight to the specifics (i.e. to the "point"), we are running the risk of falling down to a lower level of discourse. To hop from the primary to the secondary and tertiary (for instance, from grasping the key functionality of High End Audio towards a discussion of insignificant equipment specifics) means to stop "seeing the forest for the trees." It is precisely because of the syndrome of the insignificance of most preliminary discussions that people experience *total* disappointment after buying advanced audio systems so often.

As much as they try to convince themselves otherwise, without trying to figure out the fundamental reasons pushing them towards choosing "the thorny path", without striving to comprehend their own personal needs, even true lovers of music usually end up getting the wrong things. While at the same time they pay no attention at all to the equipment they *actually* do need.

It is important to understand that a sufficiently long, unhurried preparation, communication with like-mined people and planning, stoically resisting the urge to spend the cash as quickly as possible, allow one to not only concentrate and correctly distribute those resources but also, most importantly, in accordance with Maslow's hierarchies, to allow one's needs, which the future audio system is supposed to satisfy, to fully develop.

In any case, such patience will be far more productive than "audio promiscuity", that constantly exchanging bad for worse, which, in my opinion, is one of the main symptoms of the decline of high performance audio.

Resisting instant gratification — the cause of many ailments of today's civilization — one can attempt to scale the slopes of one's own Maslow pyramid through clearly focused education and self-improvement, in order to finally see Royce's "light outside." This light is the true essence of real High End Audio, without which it would be pointless to get into the subject at all. If one uses such technology in a state of spiritual darkness then the difference between all the different kinds of equipment will remain indiscernible.

In the latter case, whatever is close at hand will be randomly snatched from that "darkness." Which is what happens now everywhere.

As they say, "you reap what you sow," i.e. without the consistent self-analysis and commitment there'll be no results at all, or even negative ones. I've made sure of this many times, seeing ultra-expensive but entirely sonically incompetent systems owned by some very wealthy people. And conversely I've heard divine sounds produced by very affordable equipment used by regular listeners who have reached the peak of transcendence in their internal development and are fully aware of the purpose of their audiophile endeavors.

If one's lifetime needs have not ripened to the point urging one to reach for "the high limit" and are not pushing one to climb the sonic pyramid higher and higher, what then is the point of choosing the difficult path of *audio alpinism* and unsuccessfully attempting to climb to the very top? Moreover — to buy, as "safety ropes", an audio cable worth thousands of dollars?

In order to get to the point at the very end of this book I will employ one last example of the use of Maslow's theory for the purposes of High End Audio. Let us draw one more analogy between the "ascent" through the needs of the audio pyramid to the ascents — seemingly equally removed from both common sense and everyday needs — of alpinists.

Thus, I will allow myself to simply list the necessary stages of the corresponding "thorny path" for those who, as the famous Russian bard Vladimir Vysotsky sang in one of his most popular songs, "leaving futile arguments behind, having proven everything he needed to himself."

First, it is clear to everyone by this point that ascending to the "Peak of Audio" requires meticulous preparation, akin to that of mountain climbers, including accepting, once and for all, both seriousness of one's intentions, soberly assessing one's strength and capabilities, and the "level of ascent" appropriate to them. One needs to be fully aware that the success of such an enterprise will require both determination and stamina.

Moreover, while the financial aspect of the issue is significant it is by no means the deciding factor.

Second, everyone who is preparing to scale the "peaks of audio" has to be aware that a successful ascent is impossible — to quote the same song — without a more experienced "friend", on whom one can fully rely.

By the way, not many have this opportunity, but if they are ready for it, they can save a ton of effort and money by having this friend drop them off from the "helicopter" of his own achievements right at one of the High End Audio peaks (for instance, by selling them his own system for a reasonable price in order to buy a more advanced one).

And only at the end of this lengthy preparation can one move on and buy all the necessary "alpinist" audio equipment. Which is specifically required for this particular ascent.

To those who do things the wrong way round — i.e. those who begin by haphazardly buying audio "alpinist" equipment, as happens all the time among audio aficionados — I would quote the same song again: "better turn back and avoid the fall."

For them — arrogantly going they know not where in a hurry and as a result plunging into an abyss on their way to the peak — it will be too late to defend themselves by claiming that no one warned them, that they are no crazy audiophiles but just wanted to listen to some music...

The only thing left to them — to quote Vysotsky one more time — is to be "slightly jealous" of those who not only consciously chose the "thorny path," but will also, accordingly prepared, "go all the way that you have been unable to overcome."

BY WAY OF CONCLUSION
"I HAVE A DREAM"[1]

everal years ago on the centenary of the Russian Great October Socialist Revolution of 1917 I attended the concert of **Gonzalo Rubalcaba** — an extraordinary jazz pianist of Cuban origin — in the Grand Hall of the Saint Petersburg Philharmonic.

Too grand a date to ignore but deliberately unnoticed in capitalist Russia. As for myself, marking this date with a visit to some vulgar Russian version of a Chinese restaurant would be unfair to the memory of the event. So, instead, I decided to express my support for that bulwark of global socialism by smoking the most expensive Cuban cigar I could find — a six-year old *Behike*, worth a hundred dollars — in the morning and spending another hundred on the concert ticket (splurging on the best seats in the middle of the first row) in the evening, while visiting the focal point of the historical event — the Palace Square (packed with Chinese tourists for such a special to them occasion) — during the day.

At the concert an almost blasphemous thought occurred to me: "In all honesty the sound quality here is *so-so* at best." There was no

---

[1] Martin Luther King's best known speech on human rights and racial equality.

sound augmentation at the event but compared to the pianist's best recordings played through a more or less decent audio system — and I am familiar enough with Gonzalo's recorded oeuvre — what I heard live that day had a far lower musical resolution and constricted dynamics. In short his studio recordings have always produced a far greater effect on me.

Yes, the lowest one and a half octaves of the Grand Hall's piano[2] were awe-inspiring, with an incredible thrust and articulation to their thundering gloom. But the sound of higher notes only interfered with the perception of both the material itself and the undoubtedly remarkable performance.

Apart from once again confirming the validity of my audiophile obsession, that concert brought an even more sacrilegious epiphany. What is the point of spending millions of rubles/dollars/whatever else for maintaining something so *imperfect* (not to mention the hundred dollars spent on the ticket) when modern technology provides us with communication channels that are both of much higher quality and far more suited to our hearing abilities, and when it makes the transmission of the full range of the music's intellectual and emotional meaning a reality? And all that with an incomparably greater economic effect.

Is the only point to get us huddled together in concerts as we are in some disco[3]?

It is probably no coincidence that seeing artists perform live usually made my enthusiasm over their art to reach a saturation point after which my interest in their work quickly began to wane.

---

[2] To be fair, it needs to be noted that this historically significant concert hall has an impeccable acoustic reputation with the local academic musicians' community, meaning that my statements here are heavily influenced by my audiophile — vs academic — upbringing.

[3] By the way, from the audiophile's perspective, it goes without saying that grave "sonic issues" obviously have plagued almost every night disco that I have ever attended.

One can listen to favorite recordings hundreds of times, yet musical impressions from live performances rarely last, almost never leaving anything behind in our memory. Unfortunately, as nothing truly essential is added to the familiar studio recordings when performed live (except for some — quite often, fairly insignificant — visual experiences), a growing disinterest in the artists themselves often becomes the side effect of this disillusionment.

Naturally, there are very rare exceptions to this cruel rule, but their rarity only serves to prove it.

Since its inception High End Audio aspired to be an art form rather than merely remain within the narrow confines of technology. And, like any art form, it proved incapable of staying self-sufficient permanently — as its unfortunate contemporary collapse illustrates yet again.

Of course, we can clip High End's wings and observe how it mutates — possibly even adapting to its new circumstances and surviving. Like one could clip, figuratively speaking, Beethoven's wings — by making his music to adapt to the latest trends under market pressure, such as "back to the caves" — a particularly pronounced trend in contemporary mass-produced pop music.

In his book *Assholes: A Theory*, Aaron James said about "asshole" capitalism:

> *"There are numerous ways in which virtue can be supplanted by vice. The supplanting effect... can combine with the tendency for markets to save on virtue. The less markets depend on centralized decisions (about the allocation of resources, for instance), the less they depend on virtuous governors to make them. As Hayek puts it, the liberal market economy 'is a system in which bad men can do least harm.' Taken together, the two tendencies can induce a mutually reinforcing downward spiral of market expansion and decreased reliance on virtue.*

As Samuel Bowles explains:

'The comparative advantage of markets over other institutions in governing interactions among self-interested players... may set in motion a spiral of market-induced erosion of... ethical values, which, in turn, prompts greater reliance on markets, which further erodes values, and so on.

We thus see a degradation shift from a "virtue-driven" society to the "the only virtue is being efficient" one.

Many believe this tendency to be characteristic of capitalism and liberal institutions per se. Markets animated by self-interest, it is said, depend for their very existence on traditional familial or religious culture that encourages the personal and civic virtue needed for market-based society to work. And yet those same market relations endanger that very culture, by displacing rooted ethical commitment by market values of self-interest. This is sometimes put as the "cultural contradiction of capitalism.' " [4]

This "cultural contradiction of capitalism" is the main reason for High End Audio's current overall degradation.

Positioned at the intersection of technology and art and having its original values constantly eroded under the influence of market pressure, the half-a-century-old High End Audio industry has by now almost reached the limits of its resilience.

No art form can keep itself afloat indefinitely. The only reason that some still exist is that they are supported by significant resources and large social institutions — either public organizations or sponsorships (which are often one and the same).

As I mentioned before, the audio equipment that struck me as having the most internal passion and content was hardly visible

---

[4] Aaron James. *Assholes: A Theory (translated from Russian).*

on my sales "radar", while only the sales of the equipment that "I wouldn't personally touch with a long stick" helped me to financially survive through all these years.

Music itself is subject to the same processes. Had we relied on the voice of the "venerable" public, would we now be able to listen to Brahms sonatas in any major concert hall? I doubt it…

Therefore, given the constant pressure of the "cultural erosion of capitalism", it is amazing that some of the "last Mohicans" of High End Audio, true to their passion and artistic roots, are still alive (and that some of them are even "kicking"), having survived decades of operating in the "free market" economy.

This brings me, finally, to the key point of this chapter. Had the High End Audio industry been able to generate widespread recognition that is received by other "respectable" art forms, it would not be in the sorry state in which it finds itself today.

I recently visited a colleague who wished to buy our ear monitors. At his house, spread across three separate listening rooms, there was over a million dollars worth of audio equipment.

At the door, as I was leaving, he asked me an unexpected question: "How often do you listen to music?" Nonplussed, I replied: "What do you mean? For several hours, on almost any given day," pointing to a pair of my earphones hanging on my neck. To which he sighed: "But I've already forgotten when was the last time I turned all of these on."

And I thought: "There you go — those who actually need it can't afford it, while those who can afford almost anything don't actually need it."

Some Russian audiophiles told me that after they finished reading this book they couldn't help thinking that in fact they don't really need "any of that High End," particularly if their predominant music diet consists mostly of typical rock and pop music. And this can be absolutely true, especially if they entered the occupation for all the wrong reasons; while many those who can gain a lot from High End Audio for all the right reasons either never heard of it or, even if they did, either got a wrong impression of it, or just simply can't afford it.

It has always been my dream for our industry to, one day, emerge from its state of permanent "pregnancy" and finally acquire total freedom, including the freedom of access to its products by your "average" music enthusiasts with average incomes (according to official estimates, an average monthly salary in Russia in 2019 was around $600).

I remember how around twenty years ago the callused hands of a customer at *Purple Legion* — a young man of around twenty five — caught my attention. When I asked him what he did for a living he replied that he is a farmer from the Voronezh Oblast (a thousand kilometers to south-east from Moscow) and grows potatoes — but spends almost every evening listening to classical opera recordings (by the way, he bought then *Magnepan* speakers with *Manley* tube amplifiers).

In the context of the "free market' forces" effect on High End Audio discussed just above it's not surprising anymore that the further along the "path of democracy" we move here in Russia the less "democratic" our typical customer for dedicated audio profile becomes. And the bigger grows that part of still constantly declining overall sales which represents either one or another surrogate version of High End Audio.

Anyhow, I have not seen any farmers — or for that matter any workers from the real production sector — among my customers since then.

If High End Audio could take off its chains — a combination of consumer electronics industry's ingrained disposition to treat the available technologies merely as a source of entertainment and the strong oppression from proverbial "free market" forces — this would go a long way towards allowing itself to be treated as an art form in its own right.

The current High End Audio industry has to arm itself with the understanding of its inherent significant social benefit and to try — as much as possible — to escape the danger of the ubiquitous vicious money cycles (i.e. the way people make money is the way they spend it — so the swindlers embezzle the other swindlers in endless vicious cycles). As it possesses all the necessary means to fully reproduce the whole totality of musical experiences gained at the prohibitively expensive concert venues, it can itself become an artistic link in the music creation chain, while, like the best concert venues, offering its users the full array of instruments of the highest artistic quality.

The recently held Saint Petersburg Cultural Forum 2019 included the presentation of a project to build a philharmonic in one of Russia's largest cities — with the construction budget of tens of billions rubles. This money — a billion to a billion and a half dollars — would suffice to equip around 200 000 people with perfectly decent audiophile systems. If one considers the operating costs for such a facility, these would cover giving away tens of thousands of additional high performance audio systems a year.

A century ago attending a live concert was the only way to the complete musical experience. As this book has made clear, this is far from the case today.

This raises the question: what is more effective for the advancement of the population's overall cultural education — splurging on projects that involve global architecture stars, onyx finish in the foyer, exclusive musical instruments worth millions of dollars and insane expense for maintaining an incredible number of these "temples of music", accessible only to the chosen few? Or a more meaningful and balanced cultural policy based on, among other things, the current development of and social status of all current technologies, including audio?

For me personally that last question remains a rhetorical one — especially since the justification for these "philharmonics" requires the existence of a sufficiently large and appropriately educated audience. Given today's constantly deteriorating, market-driven cultural policy, where is one to get such an audience?

If the High End Audio industry could get past its petty internal squabbles and self-organize, then, given the very real economic effect from substituting concert venues with widespread distribution of equipment that can provide complete musical experiences, it could also realistically count on — as protectionist as that sounds — state support as well[5]. This could also include High End Audio's inclusion in public educational programs.

Otherwise, if it gets stuck at the level as low as that of primitive consumer trade in a nominally free market economy, the High End Audio industry is facing dismal prospects — the "End" part of its name will possibly become the only word we would eventually be able to hear in it.

Are widespread acknowledgement of the social benefits of High End Audio and its subsequent renaissance meant to be? Will the winds of change start to blow in the right direction? Or are all my dreams of its brighter future nothing more than wishful thinking? Only time will tell.

---

[5] Although on a different level (and quite possibly, with the opposite socio-political intentions), the government programme of transitioning to digital television via giving-away or heavily subsidising DTV decoders could be used as an example here.

TWELVE STEPS

OF THE STAIRWAY TO AUDIOPHILE HEAVEN

George Barten once wrote:

"Remember. A person should not be judged… by his standing in the world, the amount of money he makes, the clothes he wears and not even a mark that he would leave on this world.

A person should be truly judged by his or her ability to get one's own way. Therefore, set your determined sights on the object of your desires, and you will reach your goal!

The first thing you have to do is form a vision. It is a clearly articulated picture of the future that you would like to create for yourself. In other words, it is a dream.

However, if that dream has no direction, it will never become a reality. This vision has to lead both to a passion igniting within you and to a love that will be directed at your vocation and the benefits it can bring to you and others.

You need to make sure that this vision is concrete, measurable, attainable and real. As soon as you form this vision, you will need a mentor — to devise a road map with short-term objectives, progressively and thoroughly attaining which will ultimately lead you to the overall goal…

As soon as your interest flares up, try to begin following those who seem to be doing what you would like to be doing yourself. It is the only way of getting the most valuable information."

In full accordance with this quote, I am offering the fundamental principles ("steps"), adopted for High End Audio, which one can, in my own experience, rely on to draw the correct "road map" to outstanding sonic achievements.

I am profoundly convinced that only a full appreciation of the role played by the climb to each of these twelve "Steps" (i.e. being fully aware of their implications and strictly following their prescriptions) can secure an outstanding result. In theory, a "road map" like this should allow anyone who truly wants to reach the highest peaks of audio to do so.

1. Mindfulness

A clear awareness of the "why do I need this" is the key to any personal success.

2. There is no such thing as free information

If you are not paying for the information, someone else is. Not only may the interests of whoever that is not align with yours, they will likely contradict them entirely.

3. The more you try to delve into specific issues, the worse it will be for you

As the competence and experience level at the *input* of an audio system design, purchase and installation process will ultimately determine the sonic results at the *output* it is foolish not to see the correlation and continue to rely on a false sense of self-confidence.

Nothing can replace the time and effort spent by true specialists on acquiring their expertise. You will only be able to reach a similar level of expertise and experience by dedicating your whole life to it (not to mention having special talents)[1].

If you continue to employ only sporadic efforts to sift through all the necessary information on your own, then the more responsibility you would take for making the decisions the more inferior sonic returns you would get.

4. Internet Audio Forums Are Not the Place for Discussion

"Parliament is no place for discussion" is a catchphrase a Chairman of Russia's State Duma, Boris Gryzlov, said at one of the State Duma's official sessions to stop heated arguments among its deputies over a law draft in 2007. Just like the Russian Duma seems to be fit for almost anything except discussions in the potential interests of constituents, specialized Internet audio forums seem to be designed for everything except advancing the interests of their participants.

This is why most of the discussions (and especially their used equipment sale ads sections) are usually only fit to get rid of something old (especially, some useless hardware bought by mistake), but definitely not to gain something new (especially new ideas, concepts and attitudes). And if one's goal is to find ways to arrive at great sound quality achieved by adhering to fundamental truths (although, still not necessarily so to the vast majority of

---

[1] The main applicability criterion of this and all of the following principles is your main occupation. If it is not related directly to audio, then, by all means, read on.

forum dwellers) then, due to a number of the sites' typical *modi operandi*, constantly hanging out on numerous Internet forums is the least effective way of spending one's time and effort.

5. Consumer Audio Shows Are a Doubled-Edged Sword

Just like curing hemorrhoids does not require the patient to attend professional medical trade shows, curing the "pain in the ass" of audio equipment selection and installation may only be hindered by attending various consumer audio shows.

As a rule, the ability to evaluate the demonstrations' sound quality at such events is akin to the ability to evaluate the "image" quality while watching a film in a movie theater with the lights still turned on. Which is one of the main reasons (there are many more) why acting on assessments of product quality at such events, removed from the context of the other "Steps" in this chapter, can only lead to falling off the "Stairway to Audiophile Heaven."

Actually, the most useful aspect of such events is to fill some knowledge and experience gaps through direct human interaction and networking, which can help you find the right — given your specific needs — "audio doctor", who will later prescribe to you all the necessary "treatments" and "medications."

6. The Question Is Not 'What', but 'Where'

In other words, the main question is not which specific pieces of equipment one should buy but where one buys it, that is, from whom.

A brand's or product's overall quality and reputation can unquestionably have a positive effect on the end result but a far greater impact is produced by dealing with knowledgeable, experienced and genuine well-wishing professionals. Who will be able to not only ensure maximum protection for all your interests and the full realization of your hardware's individual and synergistic potentials, but will also help maintain it in the future use.

This is why the main goal of this step is to use all the capabilities of your human intuition to find and select the guiding and mentoring specialists that are the most appropriate to your tasks, whose fully reliable opinions and very solid qualifications at the "input" of your project will ensure the outstanding sonic results at its "output."

As the well-respected owner of the now defunct New York audio salon *Sound by Singer*, Andy Singer, said during my interview with him for *Audiomagazin* back in 2008: "The worst thing that ever happened to High End Audio is that we delegated the choice of equipment to the customers."

7. The Chain from Manufacturer to Customer

As they say, "birds of a feather flock together." If given the opportunity to fully mature, a product's manufacturing, promotion, sales and installation chain from the manufacturer to the end user (through intermediaries like distributors, dealers, journalists, consultants, installers and others) can be as strong as the congruence between the core specialized internal properties of the represented products and all the human "links" core personal motivations to be engaged in it.

Another helpful saying is that "the apple does not fall far from the tree" — i.e. along all the links of chains like this one, either "swindlers trick swindlers" or "selfless devotees serve selfless devotees". The chain is closed with "local" (via intermediaries') or "global" (via end users') sales feedback loops of a new demand for the product when these like-minded human "links" in the chain instigate new sales of the product at various levels via their positive feedback loop of recommendations to some other, again, like-minded individuals connected to them via their strong mutual trust.

Another saying goes that "a man is known by the company he keeps" — that is, along all the human "links" in such chains — in just slightly over exaggerating terms — either "expropriators expropriate expropriators," or "inspired inspire inspired."

There usually exists no middle ground between these two poles of High End Audio's players' *modus operandi* regarding personal adherence to the sonic truth. As — assuming that the truth is a logical *"one"*, and a lie, indifferent or incompetent behavior is a logical *"zero"* — having lied just once (not to mention outright misleading somebody) or even once not completely implementing the truth via acting with indifference or (let's presume, even innocent) incompetence — you would always end up with "zero" in the final sonic outcome. That is why, even when multiplied by all the "ones" in other "links" (in terms of the equipment choice), just one "zero" (in terms of the audio system's installation deficiencies) would still give you at the end of the chain nothing but an absolutely indifferent (*sic!*) sonic result.

Actually, this is one possible explanation for why "enchanting" audio demos are so rare — because it's so hard to eliminate all such *existential* "zeroes" of indifference to sonic truth even in the highest tier of the audio systems' manufacturing, promotion, sales and installation chains.

8. You reap what you sow

Thoughtful planning under guidance of true professionals and the end user's determination and resilience during the whole process of selecting components for an audio system and its installation — this inseparable combination of factors is the only key to success. Thus, any relapses to compulsive "consumer promiscuity", the inability to resist the temptation to spend the money as quickly as possible and the "buzz" to buy a new toy, usually end in a total failure.

Correct planning is directly related to an accurate list of sonic priorities. It should be noted that, in terms of the sonic contribution to the overall sound quality of an audio system, the uppermost priority is an initial deep awareness of personal reasons for even starting to be involved in High End Audio.

It's followed by the fundamental contribution from the complete awareness of all the correct "Steps" towards acquiring a "dream system."

Then comes the contribution from the most important and the most expensive home audio component — the listening room. The acoustic properties of a given listening space and acoustic transducer configuration within it — both in the context of home audio, and in the context of the portable one — is the next most important factor towards getting the best sound quality, and the efforts and expense to "treat it well" (sic!) usually give "the best bang for the buck" compared to all the returns from investments in any other audio components.

After that comes the contribution from a taken decision on the overall configuration of the system — either more advanced "active", with an access to a certain suit of adjustments, or "plain vanilla" variety of "passive."

Then comes the sonic contribution from the choice of specific acoustic transducers and the decisions taken on their specific physical configuration within the listening room.

It's followed in significance by the sonic contribution from the chosen power amplifiers.

Then comes the contribution from the music source selection (I skip a choice of a preamplifier as it is an already outdated class of audio components).

And finally comes the magnitude of contribution to the overall sound quality from all the other "auxiliary" equipment and components (including the contribution from the proverbial "audiophile-grade" cables).

There are some very rare exceptions in the order of such a list of the magnitudes of sonic contributions from different classes of audio components to overall sound quality, but they are usually related only to the very bottom of it.

Thus, any attempts to put the "cart before the horse" always lead to disappointing sonic results.

9. Material success is not determined by the benefits you bring to society, but the harm that you inflict upon it

This statement is the result of the distortion of the initially quite fair liberal ideological doctrine that currently dominates Western civilization and that was turned head over heels lately. Naturally, this formula smacks of exaggeration (but definitely not in contemporary Russia), but if one were to choose a certain bifurcation point in terms of income level in a given region, one would most likely be able to see that, *before* reaching it, a person would probably bring to the society more benefit than harm, whereas *after* crossing it — would most likely inflict more harm than provide benefit.

Which is why it never surprised me that the manifestation of "the soul's elation" in audio products, that appeared due to their manufacturer's desire to pursue a good cause, always contradicted their commercial success in the market.

Everyone judges everyone else by themselves and if someone earns money by lying and cheating all day, then he or she is certain that everyone else is doing exactly the same; and breaking through these prejudices with genuine intentions is becoming more and more difficult.

That's why to provide ongoing unhindered access to best sound quality it can be, any High End Audio players' truly good intentions must receive all the support they could get now.

10. The bigger the company the less likely one is to get products of absolute quality from it

From the saying "To dine with the rich you have to feed breakfasts to the poor" (by that I mean not necessarily "poor" by their income, what I refer here to is actually the vast majority of common men having the lowest sonic pretensions) it follows that the level of success of a given commercial offering in the audio market can serve as a fairly clear indicator of the intent behind its creation — all while providing a context for the customer to make the informed choice. Meaning that either you think of yourself as a "common" consumer and do not care too much about the best sound quality available or you strive for the "absolute" and care a great deal: accordingly, you will have to look for appropriate products in the opposite directions.

However, a small size of a company is only one of the necessary conditions for getting a product of absolute sound quality. Speaking of *sufficient* conditions, there is a whole range of factors, including the company's level of competence, its access to all the necessary technologies and resources, unwavering determination, sufficient resilience, etc. The element of luck, among other things, is also an important factor for implementing a specific vision in a finished commercial product. Not to mention that the product has to arrive on the market at the right place at the right time.

11. The point is not to make the right choice straightaway but to make your choice right over time

Both an endless serial exchange of bad for worse and unending procrastination that is caused by the anticipation of the rush from the next, allegedly even more "correct" purchase — these roads lead to nowhere.

In reality, consistently climbing all of the previous "Steps" described above (this is especially true of mindfulness) has to lead to the sufficiently accurate choices already — which, no matter how "right" they are initially, will require a whole range of further determined actions for the realization of the full potential of a given audio system.

12. No pain, no gain

This is my favorite one.

One has to be fully aware that, in terms of the opportunity of releasing commercially viable products (i.e. those that, in the context of the consumer electronics paradigm, do not require any additional efforts on the part of the user) the field of audio technologies has been "ploughed" through and through a long time ago, and has long entered the stage of saturation.

Assuming that only a fraction of the full potential of the capabilities of these technologies is implemented in commercial products (in most cases, this fraction would not exceed, figuratively speaking, 50 percent), any additional improvements in sound quality can only come through the efforts of the end users themselves (or their representatives). Which is why the customers, despite the commonly accepted fundamental consumer electronics paradigm, have to be fully aware that they are not "always right" (but, on the opposite, that they are wrong most of the time) and have to clearly understand the need for determined additional effort in order to continue moving forward along the path of their sonic aspirations.

In fact, this is where the demarcation line between relatively plain mid-fi products — with no claims to any determined effort on the end users' part — and High End Audio products — whose full potential is realized only via mobilizing considerable, thoughtful and qualified end users' (or their representatives') engagement — really lies.

The more consistently audiophiles act in accordance with the "no pain, no gain" principle, and the more — rather than complaining constantly about "absolute comfort" — they tread the path of some personal discomfort and consider whether it really is that significant, the bigger the fraction of the dormant audio technology potential — that has been readily available right before their eyes all the time, but, nevertheless, stayed always unnoticed — will be realized on the way to the "absolute sound."

And also bigger their chances to conquer the very highest peaks of true High End Audio.

So, finally, a quote from "Dreams of Amethyst" by Yuni:

"Why aspire to achieve anything?
Big question!
The first thing that comes to my mind as a possible answer — in order to 'constantly advance our various abilities,' but all of us will be dead in a hundred years, so what is the point?
Then how about: 'In order to grow spiritually.'
But this also only makes sense if we assume that you believe in reincarnations or resurrections of some kind, and will require you to keep all of your memories and past experiences (which is equally hard to believe, as we are always susceptible to something like Alzheimer's, which can destroy a significant part of our brain's function even during our 'mundane' life).

I think that, in the reality, there is only one truly right answer to this question: 'In order to know oneself.' "

The last quote explains the real reasons behind expending significant efforts on obtaining outstanding results in any field, including an unconditional love for music, realized with the help of high performance audio equipment.

For audiophile practical purposes, it hints on a necessity to strike a right balance between unreasonable obsession and real productivity (again, sort of, like being fully aware of a necessity to choose a right moment to leave a party before it turns ugly).

All in all, the way I see it, the Yuni quote explains the true reasons to become a High End Audio devotee in terms of finding personal happiness: as only those who have first managed to intimately know themselves and, second, live their lives in full accordance with that knowledge, can be truly happy.

48 color insert pages' illustrations, the book's front inner cover and its back inner cover (from the original edition of the book, off-set printed in Russia) can be found in full original resolution and color here:

https://stereopravda.com/books/299

#1

MISHA KUCHERENKO

"COUNTERCULTURE MAVEN"

In its December 1988 issue, the American magazine *Interview* published its "Special USSR Section" — introducing its readers to some of the stalwarts of our country's art and culture — for the first time in its history, in which I suddenly — as the protagonist of Michael Benson's piece "Counterculture Maven" — found myself in the company of poet and Nobel laureate Joseph Brodsky, chief choreographer of the Bolshoi Theatre Yuri Grigorovich, Gorbachev's top foreign policy advisor Georgy Arbatov, famous renegade Russian historian Yuri Afanasiev, avant-garde music composers Alfred Schnittke and Sofia Gubaidulina as well as other Soviet (and anti-Soviet) cultural celebrities. Consequently, along with rock star Boris Grebenshchikov, rebellious musician extraordinaire Sergei Kuryokhin, the shining star of the unofficial Soviet art scene Sergei "Africa" Bugaev, outstanding dissident artist Ilya Kabakov, avant-garde fashion designer Katya Filippova and others, I also ended up among the key figures of the local counterculture.

JOHN PEEL

I met the famous *BBC* DJ **John Peel**, who introduced the world
to such musicians as *The Fall, New Order, The Undertones, Billy
Bragg* and countless others (recognized as a veritable "national
institution" in Britain) during his first "official" visit to the USSR in
1987. He seemed to take a liking to me immediately, as it turned out
that I embodied the very purpose of his *BBC World Service* "mass
enlightenment" mission, when, tearing through terrible short wave
radio signal interference from behind the "Iron Curtain" I learned
by heart almost every word he spoke. He devoted almost an entire
chapter to our relationship in his autobiography. I stayed at his
house in Suffolk several times during my visits to Britain in the early
90s, and auditioning an incredible amount of demo tapes by new
bands that he received every day in his home studio and discussing
their merits with him became a moment when, as they say, "a dream
came true."

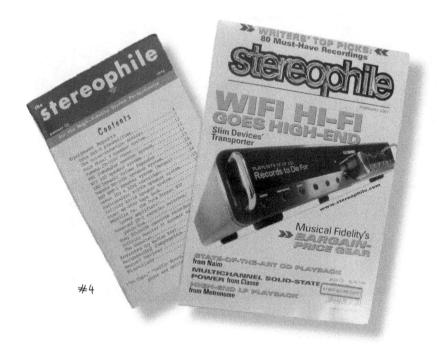

#4

STEREOPHILE

Stereophile — the way it was when its main responsibility was to its readers (*on the left*) and what it became later — when its editorial policy balance shifted towards inflicting the minimal harm to the advertisers (*on the right*). As strange as it seems, the short-sighted stinginess of the readers — who, instead of supporting the independence of such (albeit visually modest) "fanzines", which, however, were definitely on their side of the "sales counter barricades", rushed to save pennies by making *Xerox* copies of them instead of buying them — had an effect that clashed with their own interests. However, still blindly believing in the high value of free information, it appears that the vast majority of such audiophiles still haven't caught on to that simple lesson (*Stereophile*'s website address is www.stereophile.com).

#5

DAVID MANLEY

A photo of a historic moment for me — March 18th, 1993.
David Manley shakes my hand to secure the beginning of
our collaboration to sale his gear in Russia at his house in
Chino, California. Thus, as he has happened to be the only
American manufacturer who didn't avoid the first Russian
visitors to the *Stereophile-1993 Show* like the plague and
immediately agreed to do business with us, this moment
laid the foundation for my entire professional career in High
End Audio (more information can be found at
WWW.MANLEYLABS.COM and WWW.VTL.COM).

#6

PAUL KLIPSCH

This photo depicts the moment when High End Audio pioneer
Paul Klipsch, figuratively speaking, "passes me the torch" of his
generation's audiophile values (pictured with my *Purple Legion*'s
co-owner **Nikolay Schelok**). I have never been a huge fan of Klipsch
loudspeakers' sonic character, but, being fully aware of the
company's historical significance, *PL* became the company's first
distributor in Russia in 1994. By that time, it has already become
a big corporation, with constantly changing — from a meeting to
a meeting — *International Sales* representatives… Several years
later we mutually agreed to part our ways and, after a few false
starts in Russia, the company eventually found itself a more or less
proper partner here — one of the largest local Consumer Electronics
importers, which also has a dedicated audio equipment department
(more information can be found at www.klipsch.com).

#7

EVEANNA MANLEY, CHRIS SOMMOVIGO

EveAnna Manley of *Manley Labs,* and **Chris Sommovigo** of *Black Cat Cable,* are my closest kindred spirits, associates, longest time business partners in the High End Audio industry and friends. I met EveAnna in 1992 at the *Stereophile Show* in Los Angeles, and Chris three years later (this photo was taken at the CanJam RMAF-2018 in Denver, Colorado). One of the divisions of *StereoPravda* still remains the distributor of *Manley Labs* consumer products in Russia, while Chris' cables have always been a "litmus test" for me: if using them made a given audio system sound better, it meant that I was on the right track — while, if the reverse happened, it meant that something in the system's set up was wrong. This is why we only use his cables in our *StereoPravda* "SPearphone' ear monitors: in order to be sure for all 100% that we use the best it can be sonically earphone connecting cable. He custom-makes them for us, what's more — like everything truly great — almost literally, "by hand' (more information can be found at www.MANLEYLABS.COM and www.BLACKCATCABLE.COM).

#8

HARVEY "GIZMO" ROSENBERG

Out of all the books on high performance audio I've read,
The Search for Musical Ecstasy by **Harvey "Gizmo" Rosenberg**,
which he gave me at the *Stereophile Show* in 1994 in Miami,
had the biggest influence on the contents and style of this
tome. Several years later, I visited him at his house in Stamford,
a small town in Connecticut, two hours from New York by train,
to audition his own audio rig.

When Harvey prematurely left us following a heart attack aboard
a plane on his way to yet another auditioning of yet another —
naturally, tube! — amplifier in July of 2001, Barry Willis of
Stereophile wrote the following in his obituary: "...In a field
saturated with the overly serious and the self-important, he was
always a welcome source of levity, who never hesitated to poke
a hole in the balloon of pomposity..." (more information can be
found at www.meta-gizmo.org).

MAGNEPAN

Magnepan truly is the "last of the Mohicans" (this ad picture depicts their current flagship "MG-30.7"). On the one hand, the company that was founded at the very inception of the current High End Audio industry almost fifty years ago, and whose all products are handmade "from scratch" in the US, is the quintessence of the phenomenon itself. On the other, it continues to hold on to its roots. When I am asked various questions about what High End Audio is about, I would just mention *Magnepan* loudspeakers and say: "This is where all the answers are".

Including the answer to the question why achieving sound of an unusually high quality requires the equipment that is highly unusual in its appearance (and, by the way, this is only a necessary condition, not a sufficient one). (more information can be found at WWW.MAGNEPAN.COM).

#10

MAGNEPAN #2

Magnepan loudspeakers are the rare embodiment of the "good old" American work ethic that still remains in some isolated enterprises. In response to my question about the 400 000 miles on the speedometer of his hard-working vehicle, **Wendell Diller** — their head of marketing — replied confidently that they will never pass the burden of their life style on the shoulders of their customers (see their "Frugality Is Cool" ad in January, 2011 issue of *Stereophile* magazine).

The Beatles sang "…can't buy me love…" for a good reason, and in the same vein — "you can't buy me a sonic nirvana", as it's not about money invested in the relationships per *se* — it's about the accomplishments which are earned with an appropriate mutual effort. The same way, because they are already born as truly "labor of love" products, all *Magnepan* loudspeakers presume their potential customers' reciprocal ability to fully appreciate their sonic excellence. And this is why, relative to their incredibly high sound quality, these loudspeakers are so "dirt cheap" (more information can be found at WWW.MAGNEPAN.COM).

MY OWN AUDIO SYSTEM #2

All my own home High End Audio systems that I've been using
for the last quarter of century have been built around three
Apogee Acoustics loudspeakers: "Mini Grand", "Studio Grand' and
just "Grand", and all of them were "active" — two-, three (and
a half)- and four-way respectively. The audio system (pictured at
its current owner's living room) is based upon "Studio Grands"
operating in the "3.5"-way "active" mode (each monoblock power
amplifier is connected to the tweeter, woofer and to each of the
two subwoofer's dynamic drivers, the latter operate in the same
frequency band, that is why the "3.5" specification). There are eight
Manley SET-monoblocks in the system (built with a Soviet "GM-70"
direct heated triode as the output tube, equipped with Japanese
Tango output transformers, *AC* power transformers, inter-stage
transformers and "chokes", the output ones are optimized to operate
in the corresponding frequency band). The octal tube monoblock
"active" electronic crossovers for the loudspeakers, with a suit of
various adjustments, was custom-made for me by a local "vacuum
tube craftsman", **Anatoly Devitchensky.**

MY OWN AUDIO SYSTEM #3

As always, my third — and the last — own home audio system was based on *Apogee Acoustics* loudspeakers, in this case, their humongous "Grand." It was "active" four-way one: it used two built-in 500 W *Krell* amplifiers for the tweeter ribbons and the subwoofers, as well as two pairs of external *Audio Research Corporation* monoblock power amplifiers (Reference-210 and Reference-600). In the early 1990s, these loudspeakers were among the most expensive, if not the most expensive, commercially made consumer loudspeakers in the world. The total cost of the whole system exceeded the end of 1990-ies' market value of my Moscow studio apartment several times (especially, if one includes the cost of room acoustical treatment devices from *Acoustic Sciences Corporation* to tame the sound of my "audio monk's cell"). This is a photo of me (the *Apogee Acoustics* Russian distributor until the company was shut down in late 90-ies) and my "brother in arms" — **Philipp Demaret** — the former French distributor of *Apogee Acoustics*.

#13

PHILIPP DEMARET

Philipp Demaret has been a legendary figure in European High End Audio in the 1990-ies. His claim to fame has been his Chateau De Flamarens in Lavaur, to the south of Paris, where audio systems of the highest caliber, assembled from components made by companies that he officially represented in France (*Krell, Apogee Acoustics, Audio Research Corporation, Magnepan, Wilson Audio* and others) were installed and ready for a demo in almost every room. This photo of *Apogee* "Grand" at Philippe's chateau was used by the manufacturer for the cover of their official brochure.

Another one of the "absolute" sound quality audio systems from Chateau De Flamarens — in this case, based on *Wilson Audio* loudspeakers and *Audio Research* electronics. In order for the loudspeakers like these to show all of their potential, the amount of effort to precisely set them up is not for the faint of heart (not to mention the monumental special effort required for the acoustical treatment of the listening room). Should one neglect to do all of this, the loudspeakers will never demonstrate what they are capable of and can become nothing more than an expressive monument to human vanity and greed (more information can be found at WWW.EUROPE-AUDIO-DIFFUSION.COM).

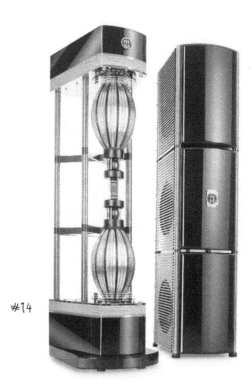

#14

MBL

In my opinion, any list of the most extraordinary examples of audio art will be incomplete without a mention of the German company *mbl*. They claim, reasonably, that acoustic waves under natural conditions propagate in all directions, which is why, at the music reproduction stage, they should also propagate in a radiation pattern of 360 degrees. With the goal of implementing this idea, *mbl* developed — "from scratch" — their own unique loudspeaker drivers, which they called "Radialstrahler" (and which audiophiles all over the world affectionately call "watermelons from Mars"). *mbl* produces the entire range of audio equipment, in every type of which the presence of the same uncompromising master is clearly felt. Again, if one agrees with my paradigm that "achieving sound of an unusually high quality requires the equipment that is highly unusual in its appearance," then *mbl* loudspeakers fully comply with it (more information can be found at WWW.MBL.DE).

#15

JOHN GRADO

John Grado is another rare example of a perfect embodiment of the old-school working ethics (pictured here at his workbench). His uncle, Joseph Grado, invented the very principle of moving coil cartridges in 1959. In 1991, John, being at the helm of the *Grado Labs*, added to the company's extensive phono cartridges' portfolio a line of headphones, which are widely recognized as some of the best in the world.

Visiting his factory — located in an inconspicuous little building in Brooklyn — around twenty years ago, I asked him: "John, why are you still in this, how should I put it, 'facility'?". "What do you mean?", he replied. "I mean, why aren't you growing, expanding your production to eventually move into a bigger space?" To which he replied: "I've never even thought about it — simply because I do not want to lose control over my products' quality."

And now the third Grado generation — John's sons Jonathan and Mathew — continue to "carry the torch" of the same family values (more information can be found at www.GRADOLABS.COM).

#16

ANDY SINGER

I bought my first truly high-end *Apogee Acoustics* "Stage" loudspeakers in 1991 at a New York audio salon *Sound by Singer*. Ten years later, I also bought my last *Apogee Acoustics* "Grand" over there too. The owner of this establishment, **Andy Singer**, has been considered one of the most influential people in the global High End Audio for many years. Due to the strategic importance of his salon's location and his personal influence, the fate of many brands was decided at his place in Manhattan, just outside Union Square. His invariably bold, on a brink of being arrogant, manners fully conformed to such his distinguished status. On the other hand, his unceremonious manners had a positive aspect: he was never afraid of being "politically incorrect" and always spoke his mind, saying out loud what others could only whisper to each other. For instance, in an interview I did with him for *Audiomagazin* in 2008, he had the following to say: "The worst thing ever happened to High End Audio is that we delegated the choice of equipment to the customers" (more information can be found at www.soundbysinger.com).

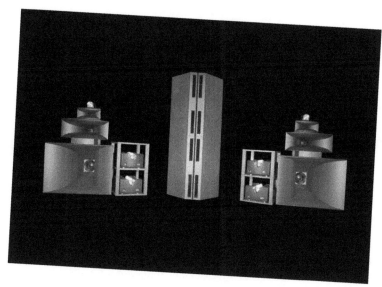

VIVA AUDIO

Leo Tolstoy once wrote: "All happy families resemble one another, but each unhappy family is unhappy in its own way." The same can be said about various technologies used in High End Audio. When they are refined to perfection, they converge in the same ecstatic musical experience. But when the work is incomplete, that is when audio reviewers start to earn their living.

True, each technology has its own specifics, but audio manufacturers' passion and sense of purpose multiplied by their expertise and listening skills eventually bring them all to almost identical sonic bliss. It's like a beautiful photograph, where the type of equipment used becomes secondary to the photographer's sense of purpose, artistic vision and skills.
In some audiophile circles, both horn-loaded speakers and vacuum-tube electronics have a reputation of vintage technologies that belong to the past. Yet, companies like *Viva Audio* from Italy continue to develop and refine the artistic sides of these time-proven technologies.

The art of High End Audio is all about creating audio equipment like musical instruments. Adhering to the traditions of perfect craftsmanship by revered luthiers Amati, Guarneri and Stradivari, manufacturers like *Viva Audio* advance and improve the original ideas of audio giants like De Forest, Klipsch and Villchur. Using new technologies and applying new materials, they make the sound of their equipment to provide the natural bliss of a rapturous and refined musical experience (more information can be found at www.vivaaudio.com).

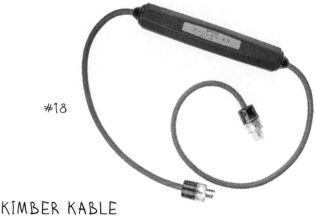

#18

KIMBER KABLE

The thing that gets people who come into passing contact with High End Audio the most is that cables can cost many thousands of dollars.

While it is not too difficult to imagine the high cost of something tangible — speakers, amplifiers, etc., — the high price of "accessories" like connecting cables is usually attributed to people "being too well-off for their own good."

Meanwhile, manufacturing a high-quality cable — as well as the physical processes that are at the heart of the sound quality it reproduces — is not that different from any other manufacturing process. The same goes for both the cost structure and the effort involved.

Nevertheless, even I, with a degree in "Theoretical and Experimental Physics," therefore, being allegedly somewhat more aware than an average individual of what is currently considered complying with laws of physics and what is not — am forced to admit that an increment of sonic improvement provided by some "passive" audio components, cables included, on the overall sound quality demonstrated by an audio system can be much more significant than I would have ever expected.

One of the most suitable examples of such a product is the "Palladian" power cable from the American company *Kimber Kable*, which can make your jaw drop from the very significant improvements of musical resolution, overall articulation and sonic image focusing, which is fully comparable to the positive impact on the overall audio system sound quality from a substantial upgrade of an "active" component.
As they say — "you live and you learn"… (more information can be found at WWW.KIMBER.COM).

MARK SCHIFTER

Mark Schifter is one of contemporary High End Audio's most colorful personalities. We are connected by both many years of business relationship and by decades of close friendship. This photo was taken during one of my stay at Mark's house just outside Denver, CO in 2005. An irrepressible energy drove him to extremes — from building some radio transmitters in Africa and participating in implementing the most up to date technologies in audio (as the co-owner of *Audio Alchemy, Genesis Loudspeakers, Perpetual Technology* and many other ventures) to manufacturing loudspeakers at a former coffin (!) factory in Colombia (!!!). As far as I know, the coffin factory project was the one that eventually "buried" him. While he and his partners were busy reconstructing the factory (to which I once remarked to him: "Why bother? Considering the lengths that speaker manufacturers go to with their boxes' designs, just put the loudspeaker drivers right into the coffins, no one will even notice that anything is wrong!"), the local currency collapsed relative to the dollar, and, as a result of various domino-like perturbations, Mark ended up in court. Having retired for a few years from the industry after that, he was reborn like a phoenix and was back in his beloved audio business. Personally, I see such twists of his fate as the best illustration of a saying that "the road to Hell is paved with good intentions". As I do see behind his various sagas his best intentions first (more information can be found at WWW.UNDERWOODHIFI.COM).

STEINWAY LYNGDORF

Peter Lyngdorf's reputation rests not only on his powerful presence in the High End Audio market in Scandinavia (where his sales network consists of over a hundred of audio "boutiques"), but also his unstoppable development of new and revolutionary technologies constantly implemented in his products. This is why he has always fascinated me. He is involved in a whole range of companies, including: *DALI* (loudspeakers production), *Lyngdorf Audio* (incredibly forward-thinking stereo and Home Theater electronics), as well as *Steinway Lyngdorf* (a joint venture for manufacturing extraordinary stereo and Home Theater systems with the famous grand piano maker).

Back in 2009, *StereoPravda*, as the *SL* distributor in Russia, organized an official presentation for Steinway Lyngdorf at the Moscow International House of Music, during which a *Steinway Lyngdorf* "Model D" system was on stage along with five (!) concert "Model D" *Steinway* grand pianos (where the photo was taken). The show's highlight was the reproduction of Ravel's "Bolero", pre-recorded by four musicians on the same spot, that included breaks — during which the same musicians which played on the recording performed the corresponding fragments live. For an additional effect, the musicians kept their hands on the piano's keyboards while the recording was being reproduced by the *SL* system. And, as they finished performing all their parts and the recording was still playing through the audio system, they got up and left the stage — creating several minutes of a surrealist feeling of their continuing presence (more information can be found at WWW.STEINWAYLYNGDORF.COM).

"HEART ON SNOW" #1

This photo, taken in the spring of 2002 (left to right: **Marc Almond**, a famous Russian musician, singer and song writer **Boris Grebenshikov**, record producer and arranger **Andrey Samsonov** and myself), depicts us in the studio during the recording of a duet performance — by Marc and Boris — of *Akvarium*'s "Gosudaryna", for Marc's "Russian" *Heart on Snow* album (on which I acted as the co-executive producer, along with **Sergey "Africa" Bugaev** — more information can be found at WWW.STEREOPRAVDA.COM).

"HEART ON SNOW" #2

Among all the musicians who participated in the recording of the *Heart On Snow* album, I had the closest and warmest relationship with **Alla Bayanova** (with whom I worked, as the executive producer, on her *Fly My Song, Fly* album in 1998). In the context of this book, my sudden strong interest in her music was, it seems, inextricably linked to the sonic experience that I had accumulated during my first few years in High End Audio. Had I not possessed it, I don't think that I would have ended up under such a spell of her truly subtle, sincere and patriotic music, the traditions of which she managed to carry unchanged through many decades of forced exile on foreign soil (more information can be found at WWW.STEREOPRAVDA.COM).

#23

GARY REBER

A good indicator of the demand for a magazine is its presence among publications that are sold at airports' newsstands. Back in the heyday of High End Audio in late 1990s, one could buy three audio magazines at most American airports: *Stereophile, The Abso!ute Sound* and *Widescreen Review*. **Gary Reber** has been the publisher and editor-in-chief of the latter for decades. Despite its name, *WSR* has always printed highly accurate and informative audio content, while his independence allowed Gary — without having to ask anyone for permission — to publish some very unorthodox materials that he thought can be very relevant to the magazine's readership as well. Such as, for instance, the lengthy interview with myself on the subject of my earphone project, which, as it happens, additionally instigated me to launch the commercial production of our *StereoPravda* "SPearphone" ear monitors in 2015, a business venture that I only had a very vague notion of at the time. This photo of my close friends — **Gary** and his wife **Marlene Reber** — was taken during one of the "Home Theater Cruises" that they organized for many years aboard the liners in the Caribbean and the Pacific oceans (more information can be found at www.widescreenreview.com).

PHIL RAMONE, ALAN PARSONS, AL SCHMITT

"One needs distance to see what is great"... When Gary Reber has been convincing me that I should participate in his "Home Theater" cruises (in 2003 and 2005), and as I was counting every minute until we would get back to ports in Florida, it hadn't even occurred to me at the time how invaluable the experience that he was offering really was. Back then, sitting at a dinner table with the most extraordinary sound producers of all times, **Phil Ramone**, **Alan Parsons** and **Al Schmitt** (next to EveAnna Manley, front row, left to right), chatting about their studio work with the *Beatles*, Frank Sinatra, Diana Krall and many others, and then listening to their seminars and demonstrations aboard the ship, all while occasionally going ashore and carelessly perusing coastal souvenir shops with them — this was seemingly taken for granted by me. But by now I fully realized how fortunate I actually was...

BERNIE GRUNDMAN

In 2017, a remarkable — and not only in terms of her biography and audiophile sound quality ambitions — singer, **Lynn Stanley** (*right*), invited me to a tour of the studio of one of the most revered contemporary mastering engineers, **Bernie Grundman** (*center*) located in Hollywood, CA. It suffices to say that Michael Jackson's *Thriller* is among the dozens of his notable mastering works. There, she played her recordings, which Bernie was preparing for release, on his state-of-the-art sound system and sang along "live" in order for the visitors to compare the real sound of her voice in the studio with the corresponding pre-mastered version of the material (while Bernie was adjusting the settings on the console, showing us different versions of the final sound).

#26

STEPHEN AMBROSE, KENNY SCHAFFER

"Birds of a feather flock together," and this photo — taken at the dedicated portable audio *CanJam* NYC-2018 show in New York — depicts me with two "hardcore" inventors: **Stephen Ambrose** (*left*) and **Kenny Schaffer** (*centre*). Stephen, of *Asius Technologies*, who I've been collaborating with for several years on implementing his solutions in my earphone products, holds a number of patents for inventions in the field of various aspects of the ear monitor design as well as inflatable tips for them. What's more, he claims that, long before Jerry Harvey, as Ambrose was working as Stevie Wonder's sound engineer, he was the first to invent the very idea of ear monitors for professional musicians' use (initially, for warning Stevie while he was moving around so he wouldn't fall off stage). To mention AC/DC again, Stephen's proprietory hearing-aid technology allowed their vocalist Brian Johnson to overcome his severe hearing damage and to tour with the band again.

Kenny's insatiable strive for inventing constantly threw him in different directions: from inventing the wireless "SVDS" guitar pedal (for instance, the sound of *AC/DC*'s Angus Young's guitar is inseparable from Kenny's guitar pedal) and the wireless principle for microphones to the release of the Russia's biggest rock singer-songwriter Boris Grebenshikov's *Radio Silence* album in the West and joint projects with the Soviet space program.

The syringe in the photo has no relation to their troubled youth and has an entirely innocent purpose: at the show in New York, Stephen demonstrated the remarkable effect from using his inflatable tips on ear monitors' sound quality (more information can be found at www.asiustechnologies.com).

#27

MEAD KILLION

In early 1992, the *Etymotic Research* "ER-4S" earphones caught my attention by being the most expensive "ear monitors" in the whole world — worth as much as $349! Considering my nomadic lifestyle, and in spite of my continuous ascent to the "highest peaks" of home audio, "portable" version of it has always been one of my primary interests. When I put "ER-4S" into my ear canals soon after, I was speechless at their sound quality just after the first split second of their auditioning, when, figuratively speaking, the singers just opened their mouths to start their part.

I later visited the *Etymotic Research's* offices, located not far from the O'Hare airport in Chicago and resembling more of a research laboratory than a manufacturing facility, with its own anechoic chamber and other advanced equipment, several times. During one of my first visits to the "factory", I interviewed the company's founder, **Mead Killion**, for *Audiomagazin*. As much as I tried to get him to "spill the beans" as to what was inside the "ER-4S" during it, I never managed to find out his secret. Mead's constant elusiveness on this subject, in the context of the ubiquitous use of "Balanced Armature" drivers in ear monitors today, now strikes me as amusing... (more information can be found at www.etymotic.com).

SMYTH RESEARCH

My interest in High End Audio began to skew entirely from home audio towards its portable version after Gary Reber told me of a new revolutionary technology of reproducing multi-channel sound through regular headphones or earphones by *Smyth Research* in 2009. It required the used transducers calibration and the listener to go through a procedure of individual calibration with the purpose of taking his personal "sonic mold" of the sound of an audio system in the listening space used as an acoustic field reference that would later be reproduced through the transducers.

In one day, I went through three such calibrations for my own *Smyth Research* "Realizer" in Los Angeles — at the historic *Egyptian Theater* in Hollywood, and two multi-channel recording and mastering studios: Robert Margouleff's *Mi Casa Multimedia* (where I pictured with **Lorr Kramer** of *Smyth Research*), located in the house of a once-famous actor Bela Lugosi, as well as Mark Waldrep's *AIX*.

Considering the stunning results from using this technology, my future plans include integrating it with our own *StereoPravda* "SPearphone" ear monitors (more information can be found at WWW.SMYTH-RESEARCH.COM).

#29

DEQX

In recent years, a range of innovative technologies (primarily digital) started to be used in High End Audio, which gives us every reason to hope for its brighter future. One of these is the technology by the Australian company *DEQX*, specifically designed for application in audiophile home systems for achieving dynamic phase coherence between loudspeakers' drivers operating in a three-way "active" mode. In addition, *DEQX'* layer of "room correction" processing allows to significantly reduce the negative impact of the listening room's acoustics on the sound produced by the loudspeakers, which is the biggest obstacle on the way to achieve "the best it can be" sound quality at home.

This photo was taken in 2008 at the *New Coliseum* audio salon in Saint Petersburg during **Kim Ryrie**'s, the head of *DEQX*, training session for the *DEQX'* Russian dealers/installers. In it, prior to room measurements that focus on bass, Kim is taking "near-field" (anechoic) measurements of the speaker's midrange and high frequency "Impulse-Response" to enable restoration of phase/timing coherence (group-delay) accuracy of the loudspeaker's drivers' joint sound radiation (more information can be found at www.DEQX.COM).

#30

MSB TECHNOLOGY

Conceptually, the highest level of a solution can be achieved when it is done "from scratch."

While, in general, the significant number of even the most expensive audio equipment uses the "off-the-shelf" parts and "OEM" components, just a handful of companies are capable of manufacturing all the principal elements of their designs "from scratch."

The American *MSB Technology* is one of them. As its founder, **Larry Gullman**, once told me, they even "cut the crystals for their clocks themselves," not to mention all the other elements of their Digital-to-Analog-Converters — input interfaces and receivers, digital filters, power supplies, and, most importantly, the highly accurate discrete multibit DAC modules, which are the "heart" of such devices — are all proprietary designs and made "from scratch."

The reason why *MSB*'s products has such unique sonic capabilities is related to the background of its founders, who started their professional careers at the Integrated Chips' manufacturer *National Semiconductors* (which, as rumor has it, built a special listening room — equipped with *Wilson Audio* "Watt/ Puppy" speakers — in order to assess the quality of the audio ICs that company produced). Therefore, as opposed to "conventional" manufacturers, who only have a very vague idea of how digital devices function at their topology's level, *MSB*'s experience and knowledge base allows it to provide solutions at the most fundamental level of research and development.

Which allows the company to always remain at the cutting edge of the latest advances in their field — a field in which products not just age, but almost become obsolete, on their way from a store to the customer's home (more information can be found at www.MSBTECHNOLOGY.COM).

VERY FINE SOLUTIONS

In a sense, you can say that the audio salons are like small music temples, where the audio dealers are like priests worshipping their music Gods at the altars of their finely tuned audio systems.

Yes, I am aware that some readers of this book can find such eulogy to High End Audio as overexaggerated, citing in more prosaic terms its benefits of improving quality of life, connecting family members and friends, and bringing to passionate audiophile music lovers a strong relief after a stressful day at work.

Nevertheless, descending on our sinful earth, I still have no choice but to re-iterate the importance of using proper instruments to find your way to the most transparent communication with "serious" music via the most appropriate audio equipment, namely, "the question is not which exact gear to buy but where (from whom) to buy it."

Frank Vermeylen's *Very Fine Solutions* audio boutique in Antwerp (Belgium) is a very good illustration of this concept. Frank's uniquely acute auditioning skills, his many years of experience in the industry and his musician's solid background make every visit to this place's precisely tuned acoustically listening rooms a Revelation.

By the way, "birds of a feather flock together," and *Very Fine Solutions* does not even try to superficially attract new customers with constantly expanding list of brands it represents; the company's relatively small portfolio include only likeminded manufacturers from the same sonic confession, for instance, *VFS* is the *MSB Technology Corp.*'s "Headquarters for Europe" (more information can be found at www.veryfinesolutions.com).

PAUL McGOWAN

It is difficult to find a larger and more successful company that makes high performance audio equipment today than Paul McGowan's (pictured) *PS Audio*. I think that there are several reasons for his success, but the main one is his extreme "political correctness" in everything he does lately: in the way he deals with people, in the precise alignment of his business activities with the corresponding waves of demand and, finally, in the lack of excessive onslaught engineering methods to design and to manufacturer his products. He recently published a memoir with a telling title — "99% True" — in which he describes, among other things, some of his troubled youth's quite "politically incorrect" tendencies, his almost half-a-century long journey in audio as well as reflects on some of the reasons behind his involvement in High End Audio and the industry's various *modi operandi*. As for specifically the latter aspects of his memoirs, let me say, half-jokingly yet half-seriously: this *StereoPravda (sic!)* book — as an absolutely "politically incorrect" one — adds that "last one percent of truth" on top of his ninety-nine "politically correct" (more information can be found at www.psaudio.com).

#33

YURI LAPINSKY – A PRISONER OF AUDIO

I met legendary **Yuri Lapinsky** at Gints Guks' birthday bash in May of 2019.

His way in audio started naturally for a boy of 14 behind the Iron Curtain, even if in his native Riga, Latvia, the epicenter of consumer electronics manufacturing in the USSR, due to proximity of the city to the "politically corrupted West", the Curtain was, sort of, perforated.

Yuri has always been an avid music collector and has always strived to build the most outstanding audio gear — from developing his own technologies for optical-mechanical centering of vinyl records playback with its innovative moistening systems and to building a rig of 10 reel-to-reel tape recorders which he designed and build from a scratch (he even took into consideration the *Earth* magnetic field in its design).

As it was impossible to buy "unauthorized" by the Government Western Music in the USSR, Yuri built an enormous network of distribution of the best sounding music reel-to-reel tapes in the country. He would receive up to ten new LPs a day from all over the world, which he would copy on his tightly calibrated ten tape recorders' rig and would send out to his agents across the whole Soviet Union.

In 1980, the KGB caught him for this totally illegal activity, and he was sentenced to jail for two years.

Nevertheless, up to this day Yuri still continues to refine his art and continues to be the highest authority of the all things audio revered by a generation after a generation of audiophiles all over the former USSR.

VLADIMIR LAMM

To me, **Vladimir Lamm** is a unique and distinguished figure on a worldwide High End Audio scene.

Having been in a state of awe and wonder at the whirlwind of events taking place around me during my first *CES* in Las Vegas in 1994, I attributed my first impression of Vladimir (based on our conversations there) to the insecurities of an unrecognized genius (especially because he was on foreign soil).

How wrong I was! And how time put everything in its right place! I simply had to gain a bit more experience to fully comprehend and appreciate how right Vladimir was about everything he told me then, and how difficult it is for really passionate people like him to get if not universal recognition but at least the recognition of their inimitable ways. This worldwide recognition of the unique sonic properties of *Lamm Industries*' equipment finally happened a mere few years after our first meeting with Vladimir.

In this book I would undoubtedly like to mention as many people from the former Soviet Union who had gained success and recognition in the field of audio as I can; and among those people the success of Vladimir Lamm is a "cherry on top," not only in terms of his company's decades of established worldwide distribution and commercial success, but also in terms of the exceptional sound quality embodied in his products' very "body and soul." In the heartwarming openness and the crystal-clear transparency of Lamm equipment's sound I have always distinctly heard intimately familiar Russian soul's motifs, and us, Russian audiophiles, cannot help but be very proud that one of us has been able to achieve all that (more information can be found at WWW. LAMMINDUSTRIES.COM).

TCHERNOV AUDIO

As Russian distributors gained experience working with audio equipment of the highest caliber, while the unwavering spread and development of trade relations across the world was taking place, the most talented, successful and determined of them became manufacturers of world class audio products of their own. Among such manufacturers, *Tchernov Audio* (pictured — the founder and perennial CEO **Pyotr Tchernov**) stands out, as having just launched its premium cable audio/video products manufacturing under its own brand in 2001, they began to sell them across all continents — and in over fifty different countries — in 2002.

Despite the possible skepticism related to their "Made in Russia" origins, the unique *Tchernov Audio* cables were met with very enthusiastic response by both reviewers' and the customers' communities all over the world (more information can be found at www.TCHERNOVCABLE.COM)

In 2018, *Tchernov Audio* first introduced its no-holds-barred DAC "Apollo", manufactured entirely in Russia as well. Every aspect of its design is based on the latest developments in digital technologies which allows the DAC to not only have the dynamic range of 145 dB but also an incredible musical resolution. As a result, this DAC demonstrates wonderful clarity along the whole frequency range and an astonishing effect of the "performers' proximity" (more information can be found at www.TCHERNOV.AUDIO.COM).

GRIGORY CHIKNAVEROV

Due to the very nature of High End Audio — located at the "intersection of technology and art" — the role of the "Audio Auteur" has always been pivotal for all the twists and turns of its fate. Accordingly, all of its future prospects are related to the creative activity of its core community consisting of its most active and talented devotees.

Grigory Chiknaverov has made the entire journey in High End Audio — from being a hardcore "melomaniac" and audio geek ceaselessly upgrading all sorts of equipment during his youth to distributing in Russia a whole multitude of High End Audio gear (both by such established companies as *Dartzeel, MSB, Kimber Kable, EMT* and by quite a few of other small "boutique" firms from all over the world), as well as, eventually, manufacturing some of its own.

For the last ten years, Grigory, along with his Russian and foreign colleagues, has been developing a line of amplifiers and loudspeakers at his own facility just outside Moscow (and which includes three large listening rooms).

In the near future, he is also planning to build his own recording studio for producing reel-to-reel tape and vinyl recordings and, in the long term, Grigory has already set his sights on taking part in creating a concert hall that would fully conform to all of his sonic requirements.

There is no doubt that, while such ardent audiophiles as Grigory — fully obsessed with their passion for music and the equipment for its highest quality reproduction — continue to be active in the High End Audio industry, it will definitely continue to inspire (more information can be found at www.GONG-AV.RU).

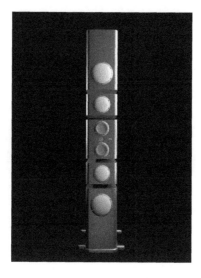

GROWUP

One of the Twelve Steps of "The Stairway to Audiophile Heaven" proclaimed in this book is this: "The point is not to make the right choice straightaway but to make your choice right over time."

To give you an example of what I meant by that, the *GrowUp* loudspeaker system, developed by **Oleg Ryzhikov** and **Grigory Chiknaverov** in Russia, provides all the necessary tools for following this principle to the letter.

The modular design of these "active" loudspeakers allows to constantly increase their sonic potential by gradually adding new modules. For instance, beginning with an initial configuration, fully in line with the current state of the listening room (as well as financial means) of a given customer, he or she can then move towards a far more advanced variation of these speakers — by upgrading the module set and changing that previous configuration.

This transition can be done from the most basic module sets and configurations all the way up to the "ultimate" one, moreover — without incurring a loss by having to sell previously bought modules (by just adding new ones). What's more, the integration of new modules into a complete acoustically coherent system takes place by simply adjusting overall settings in the system's DSP menu.

All the power amplifiers are already built into each module, while all the module connections take place via a specialized interface, so the only wires going from these loudspeakers to the outside world are the AC power cables.

A ceramic "tweeter" is used in the most basic versions, while a diamond one is used in more advanced ones (more information can be found at www.gong-av.ru).

G9 AUDIO

It really is true that, as they say, "The Russians are slow on getting into gear, but then slam on the gas." And — I would add — often "drive faster" than everyone else.

Despite all the difficulties inherent in procuring electronic parts of the highest quality in the Soviet Union, audio of the highest performance level has never been dormant over here, and many remarkable engineers used their time off from work (usually "military industry"-related) to endlessly experiment and to constantly develop new ideas.

Following the collapse of the USSR and the liberalization of the economy, which allowed to realize even the most insane audio projects, the passionate pursuit of absolute sound quality gradually allowed Russian engineers to show the whole world what they are capable of.

G9 Audio is undoubtedly one of those companies founded by three veritable audio enthusiasts: **Vitaliy Smirensky** (also the owner of an incredible collection of rare and vintage audio equipment of all kinds), **Vladimir Dyachenko** and **Kirill Ostapov**.

This company has so many ideas it wants to implement that the list of audio products it manufacturers covers all categories of audio — from DACs, phono- and line- preamplifiers to power amplifiers. They all share a common thread — the highly original and unique ideas that are realized with the obsessed perfection. Which proves, yet again, that, if you let them do it, that Russians can be ahead of the game in audio as well (more information can be found at www.G9AUDIO.RU).

GINTS GUKS

Gints Guks, or simply "Guk" (*left*), is one of the most fascinating characters with whom I've had a chance to work with and become friends throughout my entire involvement in High End Audio. Despite a slight tinge of the "freewheeling 90s" (when Guk, it seems, had to go through fire, ice and water in post-Soviet Latvia), he is a truly passionate devotee of audio art.

His right-hand (as well as left-hand) (wo-) man, constantly allowing him to maintain a state of balance, is his stunning assistant, **Monika Bokari**, who somehow manages to handle all of her responsibilities left and right: from purely business-related ones to expertly consulting Guk's guests and customers on the minute details of some obscure music.

The showroom of Guk's company, *Pro1*, located in his cottage outside Riga and constantly expanding, is a treasure trove of audio exotics of every kind: from *Steinway-Lyngdorf* systems to his own prototype of an incredible transformer-less tube amplifier, as well as a commercially produced under its own brand, *RixVox*, an audiophile-grade network music player (developed by a group of *Pro1*'s own engineers lead by **Aleksandr Anufriev** and **Andrey Tikhomirov**).

Pro1 is the distributor of over a hundred (!) of the most reputable High End Audio brands in the Baltic states. Wild birthday parties that Guk throws at his cottage are always events of an international scale, attracting a whole crowd of zealous audiophiles coming to pay their respects and have a great (as well as very productive) time (more information can be found at www.pro1.lv).

VITUS AUDIO AND DANIEL NIEDINGS

Every industry goes around a few key world regions, both in terms of production and sales. For some reason, Scandinavia has been always such an important area for High End Audio. Even in the former USSR most of the best quality consumer audio gear was made in Near-Baltic republics of Latvia and Estonia. Could it be that endless sea shores of these countries inspire the archetype of sailing to some outlandish (music) terrains?..

Vitus Audio stands out as one of the most creative Danish High End Audio manufacturers. Under helm of its founder **Hans Ole Vitus**, the eponymous manufacturer crafts four lines of equipment — from affordable Reference Series to no-holds-barred by special order only Design Studio Series.

Obviously, the intensity of the creativity field radiated from Denmark is the most intense at nearby territories, this is why, one of the strongest International distributors for the brand — **Daniel Niedings'** *Audio Deluxe* — is from nearby Latvia.

The human bond between a manufacturer and a distributor, which includes sharing the same system of values, is only a necessary condition for the success of the distributor's business venture. As in High End Audio most of manufactures are specialized in only one type of equipment, therefore, leaving other obvious sufficient conditions aside, one of the most important ones for the distributor's overall success is its ability to provide closely matched lines of components from different manufacturers which allow to achieve their sonic synergy. From this very perspective Daniel chose the rest of the lines for his distribution operation: *Transrotor* turntables and *mbl* loudspeakers from Germany, as well as Dutch *Siltech* cables and Swedish *Marten* loudspeakers — all from Baltics' major maritime Powers, by the way (more information can be found at www.vitusaudio.com and www.audiodeluxe.eu).

ALEKSANDR BALAYEV

In all the years I spent in High End Audio, I can count "revelation" demoes which I heard with fingers on just one hand. Actually, such "catalytic" sonic experiences are determined to be so rare due to the industry's declared paradigm of sonic absolutism. And as every absolutism creates a binary situation, in which there is no ambiguity or no gray area between sonic "one" and "zero", then such expressions as "almost absolute sound" should be considered as an oxymoron.

My recent visit to **Alexandr Balayev**'s dedicated listening house (!), built on his estate just outside Moscow, proved this point once again.

Among other things, this visit proved that our prejudices are built out of the gray area of imperfection or incompleteness, and at Alexandr's I had to reconsider my previous preconceptions about validity of quite a few audio technologies.

His system does include some unexpected conceptual fusions — like when the full range drivers in his loudspeakers (built by some German transvestite genius), which rely upon a long-forgotten field-coil principle of operation are fused with the latest generation no-holds-barred music network streamer. Or, like when Alexandr's solid technical background of a University geology degree (which allowed him to build a large part of his gear by himself) is fused with his reliance upon an Extra Sensual Perception talent of his friend who instructs him (over the phone!) on the correct cables' direction. Nevertheless, when you are listening to the enchanting sound of such a unique system, you are delighted to recognize that even if all of its meticulously crafted components (especially, the uppermost-quality listening room), however disparate, are in absolute technical and esoteric synergy with each other, what really brings it to life sonically is our innate catalytic mental power of absolute purity of intent. That fully palpable "flesh and blood" music aliveness, that I was so lucky — for once! — to hear at Alexandr's, is exactly what that absolute sonic binary "one" is about.

#42

REFLECTOR AUDIO

In the former USSR the Near Baltic republics, and particularly the capital of Latvia – Riga, was the epicenter of the Soviet audio Universe. This is possibly why the place is still bursting with an abundance of creative energy in the field of designing and building some of the most revolutionary audio products.

An outstanding representative of the scene is *Reflector Audio* which manufacturer loudspeaker systems for professional and consumer markets. During one of my recent visits to Riga I was kindly invited by one of the company`s founders, **Evgeny Boguslavsky**, to visit their lab and to audition one of their systems (*RA*'s another co-founder and chief "inventor" **Roland Yanevich** is pictured on the photo with their flagship Q1818 loudspeakers).

Reflector Audio has developed unique loudspeaker systems based on their patented concept that does not use enclosures, instead it relies on a mix of open baffle and horn technologies. with the lowest frequency response to be compensated with a dedicated DSP processing.

The third partner, **Viesturs Balodis**, puts it, "Due to the quality of all components in the system, smooth off axis response, concentric approach, time domain linearity and undistorted high *SPL* capability, '3D imaging' of open construction is unbelievable, with life like phantom sound sources freed in open air in the room around the listener, while many other traditional enclosure concepts somehow 'trap the sound' and give a slightly 'tunneled vision'."

However strange it could seem from the outside, the High End Audio and professional audio communities don't really overlap, both conceptually and technologically. Nevertheless, I can testify from my own auditioning of the *Reflector Audio*'s system (mostly targeted at the professional audio applications) that its sound quality can teach a lot of lessons to the audiophile community, which on the whole does need that (sometimes, quite literal) low frequency kick in the butt provided by such extraordinary technologies to wake up to the sonic reality (more information can be found at WWW.REFLECTOR.AUDIO and WWW.REFLECTORAUDIOUSA.COM).

KENNERTON AUDIO

On the opposite pole from huge corporations resides small boutique headphone manufacturers like *Kennerton Audio* from Saint Petersburg. It is another example of a reputable and enduring presence of Russian audio products in the highest tier of global consumer electronics market. *Kennerton Audio* manufactures a wide range of fully handmade headphones of the highest quality which are sold in every corner of the world. This photo depicts their closed back planar magnetic headphones called "Rognir", whose sound signature is almost indistinguishable from the one of the best open back headphones — which is actually quite an accomplishment: at all times and for all the headphone manufacturers that's been quite difficult to achieve.

Despite his extremely busy work schedule **Valentin Kazanzhi**, the owner of *Kennerton Audio* always finds some time and energy to support me in all of my endeavors — not only with his words but also with deeds. This is why, in terms of my goals for the *StereoPravda* project, not only is *Kennerton Audio* the best example to follow, but Valentin himself is — more than anyone else — unquestionably my closest "brother in arms" (more information is available at WWW.KENNERTON.COM).

#44

MY INTERVIEW FOR WIDESCREEN REVIEW MAGAZINE

The unbelievable (for its time) sound of the *Etymotic Research* "ER-4S" made me reflect at length: how could one improve on it? Its creator, Mead Killion, always replied to my question with another question, "why do it at all?". He regularly attended classical music concerts in Chicago concert halls, and what he heard there fully conforms to what he hears on similar recordings through the "ER-4S"... Moreover, a product to compete with "ER-4S" had not appeared in many years. Realizing that I would not get anything else out of Mead, eventually, I had no choice but to use my own "handy man" abilities. In late 2010, I got out the titanium casing that someone custom-cut for me at a machine tool factory; then, after several iterations, the idea of a deep fitting within the ear canal was added, then — the ear canal molds' application was tried and discarded, then the ear canal's "Second Bend" idea was implemented, and then I was off to the races...

The photo is that of the cover of July-August 2015 issue of *Widescreen Review* magazine — a historic one for me — which included an interview its editor, Gary Reber, conducted with me on the subject of our audiophile-grade *StereoPravda* SPearphone ear monitors. On Gary's part, this was an extremely generous gesture: to allow me — who hasn't yet fully thought out the idea of how I was going to set up the manufacturing process — onto the pages of his magazine, next to product reviews for such CE giants as *Sony, JVC* and others. Although, it was preceded by Gary's careful auditioning of our flagship "SB-7", still, this was, I think, very courageous of him. On the other hand, it could be that what he heard during that auditioning probably did convince him that such an interview will be of interest to the magazine's readership (more information can be found at WWW.WIDESCREENREVIEW.COM and WWW.STEREOPRAVDA.COM).

#45

JERRY HARVEY

Despite the indecisive attempts of *Shure, Weston* and several other companies to enter the top tier earphone market in the mid-to-late 1990s, Mead Killion, with his single BA-driver *Etymotic Research* "ER-4S", still dominated the global sales of the highest quality ear monitors. That is, until **Jerry Harvey** (*pictured*) came along and "grabbed the bull by its horns," doing what I was expecting from *ER*'s founder Mead Killion all along. Namely, improving the sound of "ER-4S" by using multiple "Balanced Armature" driver arrays technology — either in the form of "universal" IEMs (In-the-Ear Monitors) with "universal" tips or "custom" CIEMs (Custom-In-the-Ear Monitors) — based on making individual ear canal molds.

Precisely because of pioneering the widespread implementation and commercialization of such ear monitor manufacturing technologies for professional and consumer use under the banner of his first company, Ultimate Ears, he became a trailblazer — and the "king" for several years — of the world market for the top sound quality ear monitors.

On this photo, taken in 2016 at the *Rocky Mountains Audio Festival* in Denver, Colorado, Jerry is auditioning the first production sample of our "SB-7" ear monitors. What he said afterwards can be found at the end of CHAPTER 7 (more information can be found at WWW.PRO.ULTIMATEEARS.COM and WWW.JHAUDIO.COM).

#46

RICK RUBIN

Looking at the track record of the producer-extraordinaire **Rick Rubin** (*Metallica, Slayer, System of a Down, Johnny Cash, Rage Against the Machine* and others), it would never occur to anyone that he has always been a passionate audiophile. He never missed a chance to come to the annual *Consumer Electronics Show* in Las Vegas where he would go from a room to room attentively auditioning the sound of the demo systems.

On this photo, taken at CES-2017, he is listening to the entire song "No Worries" from Robert Glasper's *Double-Booked* album (as "a close friend plays the drums on it") through our *StereoPravda* "SPearphone SB-7".

We later sent him a pair for a more detailed evaluation of their sound quality.

MARK WALDREP

The whole of **Mark Waldrep**'s extremely useful book, *Music and Audio: A User Guide To Better Sound*, a quote from which I use in the foreword to this book, is permeated with a sense of truth-seeking and a grudge for the excessive spread of disinformation in the field of audio. In the heat of the moment, he goes after many of the indisputable audiophile concepts that are taken for granted in High End Audio (such as "esoteric" cables, skepticism regarding practical usefulness of audio measurements and the audiophile priority of subjective sound quality evaluation). His *AIX Records* label is a treasure trove of multi-channel "hi-res" recordings, most of them made at his own Los Angeles studio (which, by the way, of all the facilities in LA where I did individual calibrations for my own *Smyth Research* "Realizer", gave me the calibration files that produced the most impressive 3-D sound rendering via the supplied *Stax* headphones). In this photo, taken in 2018 at the *High End Show* in Munich, he is auditioning our *StereoPravda* Spearphone "SB-7A" ear monitors through our own dedicated two-way "active" DAC/tone-control/crossover/power amplifier DACCA unit (more information can be found at WWW.AIXRECORDS.COM).

HFN
2018

This is an article many of you, well mostly the companies actually, always anxiously wait for. This is the article in which we award the best gear of 2018. First up: My own selection!!

Best IEM (Price no objection): StereoPravda SB-7

The SB-7 for sure is one of the most unique looking universal IEM in the whole wide world. StereoPravda thinks outside of the box and it works, just try one with a good source and amp and you'll know why it's getting an award.

Review: StereoPravda SPearphone SB-7

STEREOPRAVDA

At the end of 2018, one of the most reputable portable audio Internet portals in the world, *headfonia.com*, published the list of its "Best Gear" annual international awards. Our *StereoPravda* SPearphone "SB-7" ear monitors won the "Best IEMs (Price no objection)" nomination.

It is hard for me to overstate the significance of this moment in terms of my whole journey in both music and audio. From listening to my favorite musicians on the long-wished-for Soviet-made *Akkord* mono vinyl record player for 55 rubles, bought by my mother from her annual bonus pay in 1972 — through the first attempts at reading every page of all music and audio magazines I could put my eyes on, as well as the first audiophile experiments — then, through decades of various professional activities in High End Audio — to, finally, the manufacturing of my own audio products which are gaining international recognition for their outstanding sonic properties.

I do not think that I would ever have had the nerve to write this book without having real audio products of my own behind me, the products in which all of the book's content is truly embodied and manifested — as only my own real *StereoPravda* earphones' and portable electronics' sound quality can serve as the very best estimation of how solid is the truth of everything that is written here (more information can be found at WWW.STEREOPRAVDA.COM).

ACKNOWLEDGMENTS

First and foremost I have to thank my editor **Lev Banakin**, without whom this book would never have been possible. Lev's role extended far beyond an editorial or technical function, with his deep insights and fresh ideas laying the foundation for many of the discussions presented here. Throughout the whole process of creating this book, it has undoubtedly been for Lev, as it has for me, what one would call a "labor of love".

I would also like to offer a special gratitude to my fellow townsman from Snezhinsk, **Sergey Banakin**, the owner of the Mashina Vremeni publishing house, for his active and ongoing support for this project.

As this is my first book, I would have had to constantly blush due to the indigestible form of much of its contents were it not for the all-round support from the Russian Edition copyeditor and proofreader **Lusyena Denisova**, therefore for all her titanic effort — the most sincere words of appreciation to her!

Gints Guks (from *PRO 1* in Riga, Latvia) is co-publisher of the English Edition of the original Russian book. He instigated the work on its English translation and provided an absolutely indispensable support for it, so, I can't really find some appropriate words for my feeling of gratitude which I could use to be able to express it to him!

Vladimir Puchkov of "Ves Mir" translation bureau provided me with a very substantial linguistic support to take the English Edition of the book off the ground. I would really like to thank him for that.

An international group of **Chris Sommovigo** (USA), **Kristy Song** (Singapore), **Mark Langthorne** (UK) and **David Higginbottom** (Australia) read the manuscript and provided me with invaluable editorial and proofreading feedback. For their friendly eagerness to help and for their strong encouragement that they gave me I must express my highest gratitude!

Alexandr Surayev made the final English proofreading of the book, which allowed me to avoid the inevitable and very painful bouts of insecurity of being a not native language writer. For the relief that he provided to me in that respect I am utterly grateful to him!

I have always been in awe of those authors who write clearly, simply, sharply and, whenever necessary — both audaciously and accessibly. Therefore, I cannot fail to mention with a sense of the deepest gratitude the masterful **Eduard Limonov**, as well as **Malcolm Gladwell** and the recently deceased **Vladimir Bushin**, among others, whose writing style — I humbly hope — had a significant impact on my own.

My deceased mother **Olga Dmitrievna Kucherenko** has always supported me in all my endeavors immensely, for which I am eternally grateful.

Unquestionably, I have to thank my father, **Viktor Danilovich Kucherenko**, for his constant support and can't help but kindly mention my deceased brother **Andrey**, who not only supplied me with the most globally relevant music "when I was fourteen years old", but also served as an example for me for many years.

I am deeply grateful to **Natalya Yegorova** for her infallibly warm attitude towards me and our genuine friendship throughout all these years, as well as to **Ksenia and Pyotr Agafonov** for their permanent readiness to help and constant benevolence.

Konstantin Yung and his wife **Natalya** have genuinely supported all of my initiatives lately — a huge thank you to them!

From the bottom of my heart I would like to thank my High End Audio brothers-in-arms and like-minded partners who have offered significant support for my work on this book. To me these people have always been examples of a truly creative approach to their work and a source of hope for a brighter future for our industry — in which they occupied and continue to occupy the active role of devotees, supporting any noble endeavor in the field, both technical and humanitarian in nature. First and foremost — **Grigoriy Chiknaverov** (*Gong-AV*) and also **Vitaliy Smirenskiy** (*En-Trade*), **Mikhail Samorukov** (*New Ambience*), **Pyotr Tchernov** (*Tchernov Audio*), **Yuri Gordeev** (*Next*), **Richard-Norbert Niedings** (*mbl Audio*), **Evgeniy Bezhin** and **Bogdan Arutyunov** (*TechnoLogica*), **Yuri Volkomorov** and **Andrei Viskovatov** (*ADK*), **Evgeniy Boguslavsky** and **Viesturs Balodis** (*Reflector Audio*), and — especially! — **Igor Alekseev** (*Neva Hi-Fi*).

Again, I also cannot fail to express my deepest gratitude to **Chris Sommovigo** (*Black Cat Cable*) for our quarter of a century of both close friendship and his constant support for my various projects!

EveAnna Manley (*Manley Labs*) and I are connected not only by almost thirty years of business relationships but the closest friendship, which has often led to the most exciting and unusual adventures. Any form of gratitude imaginable goes out from me to her!

My efforts to publish the English Edition of the book were kindly supported by **John Grado** and **John Chen** (*Grado Labs*), **Ray Kimber** and **Lonny Gould** (*Kimber Kable*), **Jonathan Gullman, Daniel Gullman** (*MSB Technology Corp.*), **Frank Vermeylen** (of *Very Fine Solutions* — *MSB*'s Head Quarters for Europe in Antwerp, Belgium), **Vladimir and Elina Lamm** (*Lamm Industries*), **Hans Ole Vitus** (*Vitus Audio*) and **Daniel Niedings** (*Audio Deluxe*). The list of the support some of them provided to me through the years is endless so just to thank them for the book's support would be not fair. My sincerest gratitude for whatever they helped me with during all those years goes to all of them!

I would never have been able to implement everything I had planned without the full support of **Vadim and Lyudmilla Chvertko** — for many decades. A huge thank you for that!

Sergey "Africa" Bugaev and his stunning wife **Anna** deserve special thanks as our friendship with Sergey has, year after year, helped me to always steer the "ship of my life" towards the new uncharted orbits.

Without the initial impulse from **Nikolay Schelok** and **Yuri Rebedailo** from *Purple Legion* my interest in High End Audio would have remained a mere hobby, and I would never have been able to see my calling in it. For that impulse I am obliged to express a genuine sense of gratitude to both of them. **Vadim Yantzen**, the long-time general manager of *Purple Legion*'s flagship stores, has been very responsive to all the needs of the establishment's audiophile department so I would really like to thank Vadim here.

Words of special appreciation have to go to **Gary Reber** (*Widescreen Review magazine*), with whom (and with his wife **Marlene**) I am connected by decades of close friendship. His 2015 feature interview with me in his magazine about the *StereoPravda* earphone project helped me to leave the gridlock and start to actively work on it.

I am deeply grateful to **Valentin and Natalya Kazanzhi** (*Kennerton Audio*) for their genuine help and heartfelt support, without which — especially lately — it would be simply impossible for me to deal with my own challenges, both personal and professional.

I cannot neglect to thank my fellow colleagues and close friends in the Russian High End Audio industry: **Dmitry Sokolov** and **Igor Gurman** (*StereoPravda*), **Artur Frundjan** (*Gong-AV*), **Maxim and Anna Sharpio** (*New Coliseum*), **Leonid Burtzev** (*BurcevAudio*) as well as **Aleksander Lakonkin, Alexander Bardyshev, Alexandr Balayev, Aleksey Alekseyev** and **Roman Krivonozhkin** (*Purple Legion*) for all of our deep and multi-faceted relationships, the results of which have also become the foundation of many of the ideas and events described in this book.

Oleg Volchok from *Etalon Sound* has supported me throughout the process of writing the original Russian version of book in every way — a heartfelt thank you goes to him and his wife **Yulia**!

My deepest gratitude goes to **Yuri Makarov** who helped me stick to the right path from the very beginning of my audio journey, as well as to his wife **Tatyana** who has always helped to create ideal conditions for my long auditioning sessions and endless conversations to follow with Yuri and her to be not only very productive but also very cordial.

I have met the remarkable audio engineer and forefather of our local High End Audio press the late **Anatoly Markovich Likhnitzky** at his home in Saint Petersburg in 1992. He had developed and implemented into production some of the most unique consumer audio products (turntables and tonearms, amplifiers, etc). That only meeting of ours, not to mention some of his numerous unorthodox magazine articles, especially the ones which covered a range of audio esoterica concepts, lead me to develop a number of my own ideas described in this book, for all of this I definitely should express my deepest gratitude to him.

My longtime associate — and outstanding engineer — **Aleksei Malanin** who, along with another extraordinary audio engineer, **Nikolay Ponomaryov**, sadly departed prematurely, have always helped me to realize even the most insane technical ideas, for this I am immensely grateful to both of them.

My patent agent **Alexey Markov** not only did an impeccable job helping me to receive two design patents and one utility patent on ear monitors' design but taught me a lot of lessons on how to clarify your thoughts. My deepest appreciation for that goes to him!

I would like to express my huge gratitude to **Wendell Diller** and his wife **Galina** (*Magnepan*), **Mark Schifter, Philippe Demaret** (*Europe Audio Diffusion*), **David Higginbottom** (*DEQX*), **Lieven Vranken** (*headfonia.com*), **Marcus Downey** (*headfonics.com*), **Frank Iacone** (*headphone.guru*), **Kristy Song** (*Zeppelin & Co*), **Sid Malhotra** (*Wired For Sound*), **Mitsuru Otsuka** (*Miyaji Music*), **Jeff Dorgay** (*TONEAudio and Audiophile Appartment*), **Bill Leebens** (*Copper magazine*), **Stephen and Garnet Ambrose** (*Asius Technoligies*) and **Jude Mansilla** (*head-fi. org*) for our longstanding companionship, friendship and cooperation, which have also significantly affected the contents of this book, as well as for their diverse and genuine support for some of my business ventures.

Naturally, my thanks go to all the editors and publishers who printed my materials and constantly gave me opportunities to make my personal opinions public, especially: **Maxim Semeykin, Sergey Taranov** and **Yuri Tzebers** (*Audiomagazin*), **Nikolay Efremov, Vigen Amamchyan** and **Ruslan Tarasov** (*Salon AV*), **Pavel Shuleshko** (*Art and Electronics*), **Oleg Mazur** (*soundex.ru*) as well as **Yaroslav Vorobyev** of *avreport.ru* for, among other things, their unfailing and always timely help.

The organizers of the annual Moscow *Hi-Fi & High End Show*, **Irina Nedumova** and **Daria Nedumova** from Midexpo, have organized the exhibition more than twenty-five times — without a single glitch. For their perennial well-coordinated work — a huge thank you goes to both of them as well as to a former employee of the company, **Maria Shmakova!**

A separate thank you goes out to **Sergey Zheglo** — particularly for the talents he demonstrated while creating the graphic designs for my various musical projects as well as for "polishing" the key parts of *StereoPravda*'s brand book. Also, I am very grateful to **Maxim Krasnitsky** of *Room34* design bureau for the great job he did designing "gift box" packaging for our StereoPravda SPearphone series of ear monitors.

I need to erect a monument to **Oleg Tarlinskiy** for his persistence and unshakable faith in my good intentions, and as for the value of our intellectual debates throughout many decades which has always produced the most interesting results — it cannot be overestimated!

As for my closest like-minded High End Audio colleagues, I would like to express a special appreciation to **Sergey Lebedev** who uncompromisingly supported me — not only with words but with deeds — in various situations that called upon all of my reserve of patience for standing my ground. Exactly the same gratitude goes out to **Pavel Samsonkin.**

Valery Vanyushkin and Aleksey Kashirskiy have given me a shoulder to lean on while adjusting to overall spirit of animosity pertaining to typical consumer audio Internet forums, which counts for a lot these days. A huge thank you goes from me to them for that!

My exceptionally productive conversations with **Aleksander Anufriev** and **Andrey Tikhomirov** from Riga's *PRO 1* have undoubtedly enriched this book with a quite a few interesting ideas. A special thank you should go to them for that!

I would like to express the most sincere gratitude to **Andrey Lobankov, Aleksander Sidelnikov, Roman Yakovenko, Stanislav Pavlov, Roman Khalikhov, Kirill Tomaschuk, Lev Rosenzweig** and **Sergey Babak** for a whole multitude of very productive collaborations throughout all these years.

I met **Joanna Stingray** at the epicenter of events surrounding the Leningrad Rock Club at the peak of its relevance. Our friendship — over thirty years long — and all our mutual escapades gave me a wonderful education which I am endlessly thankful to Joanna for.

Michael Benson was the first American journalist, collaborating with whom during his work on stories for the American magazine *Rolling Stone* — from UB-40 and Billy Joel concerts in Moscow and Leningrad to some interviews with Soviet hippies from the abandoned forest camp outside Riga — allowed me to take a look at many ideas, events and phenomena on a global scale for the very first time. I am extremely grateful to him for that. In addition, it seems that I have to thank him separately for a chance to avoid a stint at KGB's Lubyanka headquarters — as "hanging out" during those difficult years with many "highly questionable" personalities including himself — the son of the American cultural attaché in

Moscow — would have definitely put me there had it not been for his diplomatic status!

Paul Godfrey has always amazed me with his infinite wit and constant juggling of the most interesting and exciting ideas. Working with the *BBC* at the time, Paul introduced me to **John Peel** in 1987. During my first visit — then out of U.S.S.R. — to London in 1990 Paul not only had me stay at his apartment but also (half-jokingly, half-seriously) successfully shielded my mind — not yet strong enough for such a confrontation — from the "corrupting influence of the West". By the way, it was he — working with Daniel Lanois at the time — who brought me to the "star-studded" party described here.

Paul, my dear, thank you so much for our joint adventures across the whole world, moreover — often at the most pivotal moments. For instance, when we watched on TV the lowering of the Soviet flag and the raising of the Russian one over the Kremlin at my apartment (while drinking diluted "Royal" alcohol, if anyone remembers it). Or, for example, when I called you in London on September 11th, 2001 from a telephone booth on Wall Street in New York at 9:30 in the morning, trying to find out what those explosions thundering above me were…

A very special part of my life was devoted to recording **Alla Bayanova**'s album, *Fly, My Song, Fly*. Creative collaborations with the departed Alla and her ingenious accompanist **Mikhail Aptekman** benefited me immensely, for which I am extremely grateful to both of them.

Marc Almond and his manager **Mark Langthorne** are a different "story" entirely, and one which, I am sure, hasn't finished yet. Without them taking part in it, my life would have lost some of its brightest colors — for which I am genuinely grateful. Mark provided an indispensable support for the English Edition of the book, for which I can't thank him enough.

Marc's Russian album *Heart On Snow* remains one of his favorite. To me it was a dream come true and I cannot fail to thank all the participants of that project including the unforgettable **Lyudmila Zykina** and Alla Bayanova as well as my co-executive producer Sergey "Africa" Bugaev and the recording producer **Andrey Samsonov**.

I am very grateful to **Boris Grebenshikov** and also to the prematurely departed **Mike Naumenko** and **Viktor Tsoi** for our friendship and the music journeys we undertook together throughout many years. I must express the deepest gratitude to the inimitable **Artemy Troitsky** at whose house back in 1982 I heard a real-life audiophile tube (!) amplifier for the first time (as it later turned out, it was sold to Artemy by unforgettable **Aleksandr Polyakov** who has, sadly, left us, and to whom — and with his wife **Lyudmila** and son **Nikita** — I am indebted for the numerous hours of friendly chats and audiophile experience, gained at their always hospitable home).

Also huge thanks go to **Igor and Maxim Shaposhnikov, Aleksander Kan, Aleksander Lipnitskiy, Aleksander Sariyev, Viktor Sologub, Mikhail Ikonnikov, Arkadiy Volk, Yuri Kasparyan, Natalya Nazarova, Sergey Penkin, Irena Kyksenayte, Marinka Nikolay-Krylova** and **Sergey Kasyanov** for our musical collaborations as well as for being such inspiring and supportive friends and associates.

I cannot fail to thank my dearest friends — **Misha Veselov, Maxim Lebedev, Yuri Ovchinnikov, Artur Dmitrychenkov, Evgeniy Rodionov, Marina Konstantinova, Filipp Selivanov, "Mark", Svetlana Polskykh, Ruslan Orudzhev, Olga Khrulyova, Roman Lebedev, Elena Akselsson, Sergey Tzarevskiy, Alevtina Panikarovskikh, Vladimir Averkin** and **Kseniya Averkina** for the countless years of our mutually enriching friendship.

A separate thank you goes to **Sergey Besedin** for that historic meeting in Saint Petersburg that initiated the process of this book's creation!

I would also like to mention — with the kindest words of appreciation — my school and university "comrades-in-arms": **Viktor Mokrousov, Aleksander Lisenkov, Vladimir Khisamutdinov, Vladimir Yemelev, Sergey Khrulyov, Gleb Zverev, Alexander Pleshakov, Andrei Baryshev, Igor Kononov, Sergey Logichev** and **Rima Yagafarova**. Our close friendship coincided in time with my starting point in music and now allows me to assess it appropriately from a different time and place. In the context of this book I can say that this particular group of my oldest friends created a special "control group", that helped me to draw some of the conclusions in it.

I cannot miss the chance to express my gratitude to **Ilya Abaturov** and **Boris Pozdnyakov** as well as **Aleksei Dolotyonkov** and **Sergey Mikhailov** for providing me with cozy spots in their respectable establishments in order to re-calibrate my common sense and make full contact with the Zeitgeist of the moment.

I also have to thank **Igor Glozman, Sergey Neymann** as well as **Alexey Kolodkin, Dmitry Drutza, Artyom Erenburg, Lev Baranov, Vladimir Vorontsov, Anatoly Legotin** and **Mikhail Pashaev** — let's not say openly exactly what for here, but most importantly — for the endless hours of inspired conversations on the subject that connects us (and beyond).

To **Maxim Privezentsev** — a separate thank you for his help with my endeavors and his numerous clever suggestions regarding the content of this tome!

As for **Denis Atoyan** — I am endlessly grateful to him for the rare opportunity to see and experience firsthand the necessary human attributes required for the creation of true masterpieces!

The home of **Yana Anilovich** and **Igor Slivinskiy** has been my refuge in New York (on September 11th, 2001 too) for which I am expressing a special thank you to them here!

George Savitzky always gave me shelter (and a very comfortable one!) while I was hanging out in Chicago, IL. As we share so much in common (audiophile passion included), the time I spent with George has been always truly rewarding. So I immensely grateful to him for that!

To **Larisa Rogova** and **Konstantin Leonenko** from *ProjektSphera* as well as to **Evgeny Nikitin** and **Natalya Kovalyova** — a special appreciation from me for the many years of keeping me "in good shape"!

For a long time, **Olga Kushniryova** from *Classic Tours* and **Sergey Ovchinnikov** from *Ostravel* helped to flawlessly organize my travel logistics in every way, kudos to them for that!

I also cannot fail to express my sincerest gratitude to **Yury Gusev** and **Maxim Dyshlyuk** from the *NCIC* (The National Centre for Intellectual Capital) for the numerous pieces of sound (legal, in this case) advice they shared with me. No matter how optimistic our outlook for the future is, we still have to know where and how to "place the cushions".

Finally, let me say this. Given the initial idea for this book, I was fully aware that I would have to make certain simplifications when relaying specific technical notions and sometimes resort to a "reductionism" of sorts, trying to fit fairly complex conceptual content into the narrow confines of an overview. As strange as this may seem in an "Acknowledgements" section, I would like to thank, in advance, those readers who we can refer to as "audio professionals" — for their understanding and occasional lenience...

INDEX

Note: # refers to photo inserts

SM-103

Signature Monaural Amplifier

vitus VA audio

vitusaudio.com

Misha Kucherenko

STEREOpravda

POLITICALLY INCORRECT VIEW ON HIGH END AUDIO

In association with:
Gints Guks of Pro1

Project manager:
Sergey Banakin

Editor & designer:
Lev Banakin

Proofreading:
Alexandr Surayev

Print Digital
Paper Creme
Format A5

www.StereoPravda.com

E-MAIL AUTHOR AT:
bigmisha@STEREOPRAVDA.COM

www.Pro1.lv

E-MAIL GINTS GUKS AT:
guks@PRO1.lv

www.TimeMachineBooks.ru

TO REACH THE BOOK`S PUBLISHER:
lev@TIMEMACHINEBOOKS.RU

REGARDING THE BOOK`S AVAILIBILITY:
banakin@BK.RU

ISBN 978-5-6047502-2-3

9 785604 750223